To Peter D[...]
college, friend [...]
later. Thanks for your
involvement + [...] + for
for taking a turn carrying
the flag.

[signature]

CHOSEN INSTRUMENT

CHOSEN INSTRUMENT

AFFIRMING MEDICINE AS A CALLING

Virtie Stroup

The North Carolina Baptist Hospitals, Incorporated
Winston-Salem, North Carolina
September 2002

Published by The North Carolina Baptist Hospitals, Incorporated
Winston-Salem, North Carolina

First Edition
Printed in the United States of America
by Jostens, Winston-Salem, North Carolina

Library of Congress Cataloging-in-Publication Data

Stroup, Virtie
Chosen Instrument, Affirming Medicine as a Calling

p. cm.

Includes Appendixes

1. Academic Medical Center. 2. The Office for Chief of Professional
Services. 3. Timothy Clinard Pennell (1933-   ), M.D., the fifth
Chief (1986-2000), Surgeon, Professor of Clinical Services, and
Director of International Health Affairs (1982-2000). 4. Wake Forest
University Baptist Medical Center—the unified name for The North
Carolina Baptist Hospitals, Incorporated, and Wake Forest University
School of Medicine.
Title

This book is printed on acid-free paper.

DEDICATED

to caregivers who chose medicine

as their instrument of service.

THIS IS A SON, A CHOSEN ONE; LISTEN TO HIM.

—Luke 9:35, adapted

TABLE OF CONTENTS

FOREWORD

By Len B. Preslar, President and CEO,
The North Carolina Baptist Hospitals, Incorporated

Our Baptist Hospital began service in 1923, and then we forged our partnership with the Wake Forest University School of Medicine (then the Bowman Gray School of Medicine) in 1941. This relationship changed Baptist Hospital forever, as this book will portray, for academic medical centers are "different." Academic medical centers are truly at the very core of our nation's health care delivery system. We live and serve in the present while thinking, probing, and laying foundations for the future.

Ours is an extraordinarily complex mission carried out by highly committed individuals who live within a diverse culture. Yet the common bond among all is the perpetual challenge of operating a successful clinical enterprise while simultaneously educating the health care professionals of tomorrow and furthering the art and science of medicine.

The challenges are formidable, the rewards are substantial, and the mission endures all things. For these reasons, academic medical centers attract many of the best in our profession.

Our Wake Forest University Baptist Medical Center (WFUBMC) is an illustration of the best.

We portray our excellence and destiny through a logo filled with revealing symbolism. It is described as interlocking circles within a greater circle. The interlocking circles symbolize the interdependence of the two primary institutions that comprise the Medical Center: The North Carolina Baptist Hospital and the Wake Forest University School of Medicine.

We are interlocked because neither organization exists independently of the other. Our coexistence is symbiotic.

In the trenches, the interlocking circles also represent the interdependence of the individuals who comprise WFUBMC.

There is no other business in our economy where teamwork plays a greater role or is more crucial to success. Our physicians and nurses, technicians and engineers, clerks and administrators depend upon one another to accomplish both organizations' purposes. The camaraderie this breeds in the best of academic medical centers is exhilarating.

The inner circles of our logo have yet a deeper meaning.

These interlocking circles purposefully resemble the symbol for infinity. Our mission—our resolve for being—indeed will endure all things for all time. Our mission of ministering to the physical and mental suffering of people while also preparing future generations to do so with increasing effectiveness is worthy of our best efforts. It is a mission that appeals to the best in people and the best of people. It is a ministry exemplified in the life of Jesus Christ in whose name both partner organizations were founded decades ago.

Our logo's greater outer circle represents our core mission that embraces all that we do and bonds us inseparably for our common purpose. Our partnership is needed, for it is a stressful time for our health care industry and for the health care professionals serving within it.

This book addresses a period in the life of Wake Forest University Baptist Medical Center. It is from the perspective of Baptist Hospital's Chief of Professional Services (CPS).

The book's central focus is on our clinical enterprise, as that is the primary focus of our CPS's role.

It is our chief who gives breath to our symbol, for it is the chief who serves as the unifier—the coupler—between our two institutions, securing us with sutures for the singleness of purpose and for the nurturance of patients.

The prominent voice for this book is that of Dr. Timothy C. Pennell, our recent chief for 14 years, who reflects our mission-in-progress.

Through Tim we come to better understand the dynamics of our academic medical center. Through Tim we see the struggles he encountered as he served both in the trenches and in the leadership. We feel the joy of success and sense the pain of failure. We come to understand why our mission is so clearly worth the effort. We come to understand why the effort is a never-ending task.

If this book serves to reassure even one individual that the pursuit of a health care career is very clearly worth it, it will have been work well done. If it serves to reenergize even one member of our current Medical Center family, it will have been well worth the effort.

This book is for all those friends and colleagues who comprise the Medical Center, both now and in years past, who made us what we are and who enabled what we have become. They bring to life our values of excellence, compassion, innovation, and integrity every day, and we applaud their striving. In their own way, all are chosen instruments, for all bring to medicine the human face of caring concern.

This book, too, is for all the patients we nurture in the name of life-serving compassion. We honor their demonstrated faith in our stewardship of restoration and our reverence for life.

1 PROLOGUE: THE FACE OF MEDICINE

It is the face of medicine that patients seek, for in that human face lies their hope toward recovery of health.

It is the touch of caregivers that patients hallow, for in that human connection lies evidence of kindhearted reassurance.

Many entering medicine's healing system today give little thought to the vast complement of medical practitioners who support and protect their visits.

Most often they look only to the physicians before them, the face they encounter in their quest to feel better.

The preeminent clinical support team at Wake Forest University Baptist Medical Center is the Office for Chief of Professional Services (CPS). It deals with Medical Center matters pertaining to the care of patients, professional medical staff, and support personnel.

In the 61-year history of Wake Forest University School of Medicine with The North Carolina Baptist Hospitals, Incorporated, there have been six chiefs.

Today physicians from the medical school faculty serve by appointment as CPS's chief administrative officers for the full- and part-time medical staff practicing at the hospital. Serving with them are appointed associate and assistant Chiefs of Professional Services selected by the chief, chairs of all clinical departments and sections from the medical school, the senior executive leaders of both the medical school and hospital, an at-large member elected by the medical staff, special interest representatives, and the CPS administrative staff.

The work of the chiefs has been monumental. Their curative decisions ranged from acquiring the latest equipment for medical intervention to turnarounds during the nursing shortages to the ethics of implanting mechanical hearts and impregnating eggs for human life to the safety of patients and staff from the devastation of infectious diseases to research into the secrets lying within human genes.

The chiefs' leadership portrays their never-ending commitment to the betterment of health care delivery. The chiefs triumphed in spurring on that progress during times described as their "own season," and they often were the adhesive that held the two maturing institutions together as they honed unity.

They had talents needed during their seasons to assist the Medical Center's growth toward excellence and prominence. They were chosen instruments in that attainment. And each stepped down when he recognized that his season was over, as did Dr. Timothy C. Pennell, the fifth chief, on June 30, 2000.[1]

It is Pennell's voice that was chosen to narrate the work of the Chief of Professional Services here at the onset of the 21st century.[2] He speaks for all who carry out the work of the Chief of Professional Services on an hourly and daily basis. Here within his words also is the story of a physician who chose the instrument of healing as his ministry while also serving as chief, surgeon, professor, international health promoter, and beloved friend in deed toward those with whom he served.

He discloses problems in medicine that patients often do not see and hopefully never will. He shares memories of nearly 50 years associated with the Medical Center. That includes 18 years with the Office for Chief of Professional Services—14 as chief and four on its executive committee—over 40 years as physician, surgeon, and professor of surgery, and over 19 years as director of the Office of International Health.

Chosen Instrument is the story of his personal partnership with the Medical Center and with medicine, told for all those who seek the humane and honored healing care found there.

Over the years many individuals during their seasons of giving have secured this continuum of compassionate care that today is fondly called "The Miracle on Hawthorne Hill." Without their immeasurable contributions and devotion—especially those by the chiefs—this legend would not have been possible or preserved.

[1] The current and sixth Chief of Professional Services is Dr. Vardaman M. Buckalew Jr., a nephrologist who is a professor of Nephrology and of Physiology and Pharmacology at Wake Forest University School of Medicine. His term as chief began July 1, 2000.

[2] See the Appendixes for books explicitly on the history of Wake Forest University Baptist Medical Center.

II THE CONTINUUM OF PRESERVERS

The Chief of Professional Services (CPS) is an awesome appointment simply because of the interdependence between The North Carolina Baptist Hospitals, Incorporated and Wake Forest University School of Medicine.

In most medical centers, the post is broken into two positions: clinical dean for the medical school and chief of staff for the hospital. Twelve years after the two came together, in 1953, the name was changed from medical director to its current title.

The CPS is the chief administrative guardian of quality care for patients and for quality environment and equipment for clinical faculty and staff serving the hospital. He or she also is the developer of more flexible health care teams and communicator between the two houses of the Medical Center.

The chief—up to the present all have been men—and associates, all from the clinical faculty, work as a team with a hospital representative in directing the medical staff services and quality consulting. This CPS team is responsible for seeing that all professional services within the complex operate properly and orderly.

CPS's jurisdiction spills over into hospital administrative areas as well as medical school academic matters.

There is no way to train to be Chief of Professional Services except by performing its tasks, by coming up through the ranks in services rendered, or by election to the CPS executive committee—and by being able to distinguish between urgent and imperative.

The chief does not have unlimited decision-making powers, but his expertise very often has been tapped because of personal overall knowledge of the operation of the institutions.

Those who hold the post carry out its breadth and determine its depth according to medical demands. Routinely this involves dealing first with politics and diplomacy.

The chief currently is collaboratively appointed to a one-year term, renewable each November, by the president and chief executive officer for Wake Forest University Health Sciences, Dr. Richard H. Dean, and by the president and chief executive officer of The North Carolina

Baptist Hospitals, Len B. Preslar Jr. They select the CPS in consultation with the medical school dean, Dr. William B. Applegate,[3] faculty chairs of medical school departments and sections, and other appointed representatives from the institutions.

It may be that in the future the function of the chief's office will be redefined as the result of a new affiliation agreement between the medical school and hospital now being implemented as part of the Medical Center's current realignment process.

The hospital and the university and its medical school entered this harmony pledge in order to provide total excellence in medical care, education, and research.

In the realignment agreement, they acknowledged and affirmed their substantial *inter*dependence but also recognized their *in*dependence as separate corporations that control their own affairs and property. While not in legal partnership, the two institutions serve in close overarching cooperation to promote effective and efficient services, both clinical and administrative, that enhance their mission as one of the nation's top academic medical centers.

Under the agreement, Baptist continues to provide high quality inpatient facilities and a full range of services and support for patient care and related programs inherent in a teaching hospital, including graduate medical education. The medical school continues its high standards for programs in teaching, research, and clinical endeavors and provides an accomplished clinical faculty to serve as the hospital's medical staff.

Both institutions continue to provide superior comprehensive and competitive outpatient services while sharing equally in responsibilities, obligations, and authority in order to optimize performance and success and to avoid unnecessary duplication.

Within this cooperative agreement, both institutions are parallel in authority. Their relationship is founded on principles of accountability, discipline, and mutual benefit. In the event of conflict, the Medical Center's senior executives serve as mediators.

History has shown that the two enterprises in their coexistence have

---

[3] Dr. Applegate became dean of Wake Forest University School of Medicine and senior vice president of Wake Forest University Health Sciences on April 1, 2002, succeeding Dr. James N. Thompson, an otolaryngologist, who served as dean from 1994 to 2001. Applegate came to the medical school in January 1999 to be a professor and chairman of the Department of Internal Medicine. He also was co-chair of Wake Forest University Physicians (WFUP), which governs the clinical faculty.

kept step with progress, quality, and accomplishments, and that advancement is due in part to the leadership by the Chiefs of Professional Services.

For the chiefs over the years have been the needed bridge uniting the hospital and the physicians. From their angle-of-unity vision, the chiefs realized the need to perform their CPS duties with total equity, conformity, and inclusiveness.

It is a process that has worked and worked well. CPS leadership has helped this house of healing not only to survive but also to hum. Longtime observers admit freely that it was "the chiefs who held us together and got us over our day-to-day hurdles."

Those who came to serve with them got their eyes opened, for they came to learn how things got done cooperatively between the institutions and how the processes involving management, planning, resources, equipment, buildings, and personnel were handled. And how the institutions dealt with the major problems and challenges facing them. They learned also that a lot of the quality so evident within the Medical Center, particularly as it relates to patient care, began with the chiefs and their perpetual caretaking.

The Medical Center has been fortunate with its chiefs who were there to nurture the institution during times of unbelievable advancements, financial perils, devastating health issues, and autocratic outsiders. The role of chief often approaches a full-time position, but each chief remained dedicated foremost to his profession. How he interpreted his secondary commitment as CPS was a personal decision.

When Dr. Eben Alexander, a neurosurgeon, was designated as the first chief, he took the appointment to a heterogeneous level. For 20 years, 1953-1973, he kept a vigilance open to need, correction, and detail. He held the position when the double-harnessed institutions were young, building, and yet to establish their full direction.

To this day he still sustains incredible devotion and love for the place. It remains his weekday work home. He continues to write papers on his lifetime research into the neurosciences. At 89, he is considered CPS emeritus. His analytical eyes still overlook the Medical Center's operation and he continues to remind all leaders of things that need to be fixed if the complex is to operate proficiently.

Many of Alexander's CPS assignments dealt with money: to maintain first-class patient care despite the hospital's financial deficit, to balance facility and patient needs, to pay an enlarging medical faculty, and to enhance physicians' fees for services. He held the rudder as the two institutions embarked on a more effective partnership.

His integrity and leadership were often needed when these matters erupted and affected the stability and future of the Medical Center. He could be conciliatory and persuasive but never intimidated.

In the early 1970s, he increasingly took over the administration of the hospital as Reid T. Holmes, the administrator for 29 years, slowly succumbed to the devastation of the then little-known Alzheimer's disease. Both were partners in bringing the young facility to an established hospital and both were successful in making its reputation recognized. Alexander was determined to maintain that prominence.

Daily he walked through the hospital's business and admitting offices to evaluate patient admissions, review what bills could be paid, and determine if employees—he often knew them by name and position—were doing their job. His astuteness for detail assisted his task of keeping the Medical Center afloat. He was supported in this very, very difficult time by the leadership of both institutions.

That reciprocal cooperation would later benefit the Medical Center and its reputation of excellence.

Race was an issue during his tenure as it applied to people of color sharing the same patient room with whites. From history's vantage today this seems petty, but for the chief in the early 1950s the question was, "Do we keep blacks in one room and whites in another?" Blacks were never segregated to all-black wards. Soon Baptist adopted an open-occupancy policy—well before mandated by federal law.

While CPS, Alexander also was building his reputation as an internationally known neurosurgeon and clinical researcher in children's neuropathy. Under his guidance while head of the Section on Neurosurgery, the Medical Center gained recognition as having one of the best neurosurgery residency programs in the nation. He was recognized by the Society of Neurological Surgeons, which elected him president in 1972. This society and the American Medical Association bestowed Distinguished Service Awards on him in 1989.

Twenty years as chief made him an institution within an institution. No other chief has served that long. Alexander was most powerful at his chosen time.

His contribution to quality patient care is still a must and his successors have kept that watch.

He was appointed chief by Dr. Coy C. Carpenter, dean at Wake Forest's school of medicine (1936-1963) and vice president for health affairs for its parent institution, Wake Forest College (1963-1967) that later became Wake Forest University, and the first medical director for the four-year medical school (1939-1951).

Carpenter was the grail-keeper in the move of the medical school to Winston-Salem and four-year competency. It became the greatest challenge of his life. He dreamed the dream and persevered in giving it life support.

He also helped to give birth to a second blessing: bringing the college to Winston-Salem to rejoin its medical school.

Today he is still acknowledged as the one person who did more than any other to give the medical school its birthright of distinction. He did not have an easy time transforming his dreams into reality, but he did have an abundance of optimism, far-sightedness, courage, tenacity, and power.

His greatest challenge was financial, a relapse illness in the history of both the medical school and its teaching hospital. But he knew the right people and the right sources for obtaining funds for services rendered. Furthermore he had the cocksureness to access both. Even after retiring, he kept his title of fund-raiser extraordinaire.

Dr. Frank R. Lock, the only other medical director (1951-1953), served between Carpenter and Alexander. He also was associate medical school dean during this period.

Lock was only 31 when he came to the medical school in 1941 to become the first chair in the Department of Obstetrics and Gynecology and to establish a research program in that area. This dynamic and hardworking physician is still remembered for being a great teacher, skilled surgeon, humanitarian, and motivator for medical students.

In 1965 he served simultaneously as president of the American College of Obstetricians and Gynecologists and the American Association of Obstetrics and Gynecology. He was the first president of the Bowman Gray Foundation, established to promote medical education and training for physicians, technicians, nurses, and scientists; to enhance research; and to improve facilities at the Medical Center. His experience as medical director enhanced this work, for he had seen need firsthand.

As medical director, Lock worked with Holmes. Alexander was chief first with Holmes and then with his successor, John E. Lynch, who served as executive vice president (1970-1972), CEO (1972-1987) and president (1974-1987) of the hospital, and co-director of the Medical Center (1983-1987).

Lynch's incisiveness is another example of serving in one's own season.

He came at a time when the hospital met its payroll on borrowed money. No one can ever dispute the fact that he turned the place around financially. He wanted full control of the hospital; he did not need a working CPS. What he needed was someone from the medical side with whom to consult and mediate.

His fortuitous leadership stabilized the hospital (and bilaterally the medical school) and set it on a path toward recovery. The hospital's eminent financial potency of today began with Lynch.

He set an agenda of constraint. He demanded efficiency—first-rank patient care at the lowest price—and drastically reduced duplication. Those measures allowed him to generate reserve funds and to establish new health service programs for the Medical Center.

Never again did he want the hospital beholden to anyone for daily financial needs. Never again did he want physicians needing to share their income so that others might be paid or receive care. Medical Center leaders supported these directives.

Despite others' views, he believed efficiency would enhance quality and it did—to the degree allowed under the conservative economy he exercised.

His approach proved to be his most profound achievement, bought at a price.

Many felt restrained and irritated by Lynch's frugalness and management style, so a bitter feeling began to grow between the institutions. Their relationship was strained to an in-law syndrome.

The next Chief of Professional Services was caught in the middle of this turbulence. Plus, he followed the longtime era of eminence held by Alexander.

But once again the new chief, Dr. Thomas H. Irving, was the man for his season.

When Dr. Manson Meads,[4] medical school dean and director of the Medical Center, picked him as the second CPS, Irving was chair of the Department of Anesthesia (1969-1982). He came to the medical school in 1967 to head the Section on Anesthesia in the Department of Surgery. Because he had demonstrated outstanding academic, clinical, and administrative abilities, the section was elevated to full departmental status two years later with Irving as chair. Irving would need these skills as CPS (1973-1977). He made himself available for consultation with the hospital administration, but he did not want to be a full-time working chief. The Medical Center was expanding its campus and its services in double-quick time, so its leaders no longer could practice solo decision making.

---

[4] It is appropriate early in this book to honor, as did all those interviewed, the astonishing contributions, sung and unsung, of Dr. Meads. During 24 years of executive leadership at the Medical Center, he accomplished amazing things in a very quiet non-self-serving manner. His deeds left footprints for others to find and follow in their paths toward exceptional service. Dr. Meads died July 8, 2001.

Irving became a facilitator. He did not want to rule aggressively or oppressively, for he was a very peaceful individual. He did not want to give advice to the hospital on how to operate its business.

It was a very stormy time on the Hill and the illness was fear that the hospital was going under.

Irving took the brunt of this spoken fear and revitalized communications between the hospital and medical staffs. He found this to be the adhesive-bonding link needed for better understanding. At weekly luncheons, concerns were laid on the table as part of the menu. Participants became aware—often for the first time—of the compendious issues being faced across the campus. Irving liked problem solving and was good at it. He enjoyed finding answers. The relationship between the two staffs became closer.

Before making a decision, Irving sought opinions on an issue; he seldom revealed his own. Some thought he ignored the clinician, but he never ignored anything. He was just very careful in what he selected to get done and when he addressed it. He very carefully triaged what he thought were the priority requests from the medical staff, such as the trouble physicians were having with the hospital's admitting office.

He became a David in the Goliath struggle between motive and authority so prevalent then at the Medical Center. Like David, he was an admirable administrator. He often used humor as levity. He remained fair in his leadership, but he would not be manipulated. He could be firm, as exemplified by his admonition to his colleagues to watch their conversations in elevators and hospital corridors where the public discussion of patient cases was off-limits.

It was an unusual time. The leadership above CPS was composed of longtime decision makers who by necessity were forced to base progress on caution. Irving, Lynch, and Dr. Richard Janeway, who became medical school dean in 1971 (and later executive vice president of health affairs, 1983-1997, and co-director of the Medical Center, 1983-1997), were all very young men at the helm of an increasingly large and significant complex. Their youthful energies were needed.

It was a time when the Medical Center campus was undergoing massive construction and restructuring projects made possible by the Medical Center Challenge Fund. For example, when the medical school added the Department of Family Medicine, a building was needed to house the work and staff. It also accommodated a newly enlarging medical student body.

Medicare and Medicaid brought new patients and new health care problems. Soon this Medical Center, as well as others in the nation, began to feel a raw new emotion flung at them by the public: anger. It was patient reaction to insurance providers who had no face. That anger is now close to a heart-attack stage.

Physicians today—and since Irving's time—have to push these emotions aside in order to remain faithful to their commitment to give their very best to patient care despite illnesses, insurance coverage, and patient displeasure.

Quality patient care was a major theme of Irving's tenure—wherever dispensed. He monitored that care carefully. Where there were deficiencies, he tried to eradicate them. Another zeal was helping the medical staff understand the very difficult financial decisions Lynch was facing—and Irving was good in this role.

His successor, Dr. Robert N. Headley (1977-1981), took that zeal to an even higher level: No other chief ever had better insight into the financial workings of the hospital. And as he learned, he shared information with his colleagues.

Janeway appointed Headley and they had a very good working relationship. During Headley's season, he became intricately involved in Lynch's work world.

A major problem for Headley—both as head of the Section on Cardiology and as CPS chief—was the hospital's very first critical shortage of nurses.

The hospital closed its School of Nursing in 1974 because it became too expensive to operate. Without in-house training and therefore an ever-available supply of nurses, the hospital began offering inducements to attract them: incentive pay, fringe benefits, and more flexible work hours. The nursing shortage was a national issue.

Headley worked very closely with the hospital's administrator to determine what surgical procedures could be scheduled according to the daily nurse-to-patient census.

As the shortage decreased, Headley encouraged physicians to seek new patients. He sent them out into the community so that they were more visible. People became aware of the hospital's reputation as a house of healing in many disciplines. He followed his own advice and soon was admitting more patients than any two physicians combined. At one time he was known as the busiest physician at the Medical Center— more patients, more admissions, more discharges.

He knew that additional patients meant additional revenue.

This CPS took an in-depth look at the nursing situation and realized that incentives needed to be issued across-the-board if *all* health professionals were to be induced to join this growing medical haven.

Internally, the two institutions realized if they were to have a shared future, they would need a shared vision and that would require shared cooperation. Headley worked incessantly to get both groups to see the mutual advantage of moving ahead with new expertise, new technologies, and a first-class working environment. Both mutually agreed to share in funding a center of excellence.

The road to this goal was paved with monetary fright. After all they had just come out of financial rehabilitation. If they hadn't been a charitable organization, they would have died in foreclosure. Headley spent time, again and again, encouraging Lynch—often to the level of coercing him—to use some of his reserve funds as seed money for new programs to upgrade medical care and to invest in new services that would put them on the cutting edge of superior health delivery. Lynch made these funds available.

After all, this no longer was a community hospital but a major tertiary medical center that trained physicians and caretakers, participated in research of note, and offered the highest level of medical care.

In his specialty, Headley was trying to get a cardiac care unit started. He was having difficulty finding funding for the unit and for equipment needed in a teaching hospital. He had a keenness for therapy readiness, for he came up in his field when cardiopulmonary resuscitation, defibrillators, and pacemakers were not yet available. His dream for a cardiac care unit became a reality and today has become a security blanket for those needing its help and for enlarging another prime specialty for the Medical Center's roster.

Headley saw his role not as one of autonomy or dictatorship but mainly as the liaison between the two giant corporate bodies, so he became a compromiser and negotiator, trying to achieve superb medical care within a united enterprise.

He and Lynch saw the need and then established the capital equipment budget committee, funded annually by the hospital. The medical and hospital staffs became very competitive for these limited funds in their quest for new and innovative technology, for upgrades or replacements in the physical plant, and for new medical instruments to support these proposals.

The Faculty Executive Council and CPS reviewed the proposals, prioritized them, and granted them on the basis of need, quality, and availability of funds.

So in addition to being clinically brilliant, Headley as CPS was financially brilliant. Daily he met with hospital leaders, reviewing hospital balance sheets, census records, and operations scheduled. What he didn't understand, he questioned. He learned how the hospital operated. He came to understand its billing system and profit margins. He knew how to read the hospital's financial books, so he knew how much money it was making. Then he used that information for the betterment of the total Medical Center.

He, too, knew when it was time to step down as CPS. He and Irving later served as associate chiefs, so their expertise continued to be tapped.

Dr. Courtland H. Davis Jr. came into his season in 1981 as the hospital's fourth chief. During his five-year tenure, this neurosurgeon, as well as all chiefs, shared the hallmark of being an active clinician while CPS. He was highly regarded and respected in his field and by referring physicians.

Before appointment by Janeway, he was assistant chief under Irving and Headley from whom he learned the functions of the office. His on-the-job training allowed him to meet the burdens of the office with a better understanding of how-to.

His assistant chiefs were Dr. James N. Thompson, an otolaryngologist who later served as dean of the medical school (1994-2001) and as a university vice president (1997-2001), and Dr. Patricia L. Adams, a nephrologist who now is the medical school's associate dean for student services.

It is inconceivable that any of the chiefs could have held the Medical Center on its rise to salience without the team efforts, assistance, and admonition of the CPS's associate and assistant chiefs, departmental chairs, and the contributions made by study committees that served over the years. Davis, as do all the chiefs, totally acknowledges this partnership and dependence.

Davis' aura was that of a perfect gentleman, never showing anger, disrespect, or abruptness. He approached CPS issues with considerable thought and endeavored to make even-handed decisions.

He had one very strict medical rule: Under no circumstances was he ever to be disturbed while in the operating room or clinic. In his thinking, CPS paperwork left undone would not kill a patient. He felt his attention belonged first to the patient.

Davis was a great diplomat when solutions were needed for difficult problems, but he did not get overly involved in the finances or operations of the hospital.

It was a time when the medical staff needed a lot of nurture and he gave it. He spent his energies keeping that staff abreast of daily happenings. He rerouted any data he received from the hospital administration, for he believed in sharing information openly and honestly.

His memos often beat the rumor mill and as a result the medical staff became a closer group. It led to better relationships and communications between the hospital and medical staffs.

Quietly and uncontentiously, he kept the Medical Center on an even keel, keeping it from listing to one side of the two institutions.

That was unbelievably hard, considering the assiduous personalities of those with whom he worked all across the campus.

He was at the helm when ambulatory and same-day surgery became the norm and intermediate care units became a necessity. Other additions on his watch included the air-ambulance services of AirCare, the acquisition of vanguard equipment, such as the lithotripter for the dissolution of kidney stones and gallstones, and the upgrading of the computerization of the Medical Center.

It was time, too, for establishing an ethics committee. Late in Davis' service, a study group began looking into "do not resuscitate" (DNR) and withholding cardiopulmonary resuscitation orders, privacy of genetically identified diseases, transplant surgery, irreversible coma and terminal illnesses, and foregoing life-sustaining treatment for seriously ill newborns or babies seriously handicapped, and living will guidelines.

Davis wanted to insure that CPS was a functioning committee because medical services were becoming broader, more specialized, and certainly more patient involved; because illnesses were recognized as encompassing more organ systems; and because medical research was uncovering new causes of illnesses and new treatments. The Medical Center needed guidelines to follow when these medical emergencies occurred.

CPS's work in this area was begun before the Federal Self-Determination Act of 1991. That federal law required hospitals to adopt policies on patients' rights to make decisions concerning medical care and to keep those directives in patients' chart files.

A year into Davis' tenure, CPS adopted a policy that cardiopulmonary resuscitation (CPR), an emergency lifesaving method for persons in cardiac or respiratory arrest, be performed unless specific orders were written to the contrary.

Before he was chief, Davis asked CPS to consider a restricted smoking policy for the Medical Center. In 1992, after Davis' tenure, an all-encompassing smoking policy for patients, visitors, and employees engaged in hospital activities was adopted in response to a smoke-free requirement made by the Joint Commission on Accreditation of Healthcare Organizations. Under this plan, Baptist Hospital included a compassionate provision, approved by CPS, that allowed smoking for the terminally ill, especially if abstinence would interfere with intended medical care.

Since then, the smoking policy has become more stringent: No tobacco products are now sold in any hospital building, and smoking is allowed only at designated outdoor areas. Smoking violations are reported to CPS.

In 1994, the medical school began a program teaching its third-year students how to help their patients to quit smoking. Today it is one of only three medical schools in the nation offering a required course on the physiology of nicotine addiction.

It also was keeping-up time at the Medical Center: trying to accommodate the increased patient and referral load, purchasing more sophisticated paraphernalia, providing the latest in therapeutic treatment, and expanding medical education while obtaining new faculty specialists and research giants.

And concurrently, the Medical Center was moving into its largest era of reorganization.

The fight-for-survival era became a fight-for-identity consideration, beginning with Wake Forest University's move to a covenant-only relationship with its founder, the North Carolina Baptist State Convention, the same group that started the hospital (a relationship that is still maintained). The Medical Center envisioned its future and steered its course toward benchmark distinction.

So it became navel-gazing time: "Where was the Medical Center going in the future?" "Would the hospital stay independent?" "Would the medical school preserve its umbilical-cord attachment to the university?" "Would the university medical school and hospital ever become truly one?"

The injuries from this tug-of-war were not easily remedied at this major tertiary care center. The environment became very political. Davis, the gentle-hearted, recognized his season was over.

Onto the scene in 1986 came the fifth chief. Dr. Timothy C. Pennell was perfect for his season and in his role as political emancipator. He became the needed liaison and interpreter between Lynch and Janeway and then between Preslar and Dean.

He assisted them as they recognized their relatedness despite their separateness. He worked to maintain the standards of quality as the Medical Center expanded.

He was the embodiment of the best traits of all his predecessors, often using these distinctions to elevate the Medical Center's place in accomplishments. He had the prodigious ability to hear need and meet it before it festered into a squawking impasse. And he was able to separate prattle and rhetoric between the two institutions when ties would bind. By nature an activist free of bias, he aggressively addressed issues as new as today's newspaper and as old as yesterday's edition. He refused to retreat from controversy, shoddiness, disparity, or crises. And he was free from prejudice and discrimination.

His accessibility is legendary. He used his divined skills to eliminate problems and to get answers or to suggest alternatives.

Plus, he brought into the office firsthand understanding of his Baptist faith and its willingness to provide excellence in human care. This is a dualism he shares with Preslar, the hospital's current money empowerer who helps steer both institutions toward renewed and infrangible stability and steady access toward increased growth and quality.

Preslar has moved the hospital from a more conservative status financially to a more aggressive conservational position—saving founding principles and fostering a more open unity with the medical school while maintaining quality and amplifying care and services during the staggering evolutionary changes medicine now is encountering.

And so today the Medical Center is more fundamentally sound and has reached its winner's category by becoming one of the nation's very top academic medical centers.

CPS endeavored to perpetuate and stabilize this level of accomplishment, for it recognized medicine no longer can be practiced as usual. Being good has been replaced by being better. Today this competency level has moved to being among the best. And Pennell was among those who helped.

As chief, he was adept as a critically needed mediator and negotiator. People who were mortal enemies equally loved and respected him. At the medical arbitration table, he extracted resolution from conflict—something he learned from the Bible. He listened to all sides of an issue, pulled opinions from everyone, and found common-ground solutions. It was an earned talent. It is one thing to be a person with ideas and energy, but he no longer could be just the lovable doctor. As chief, his recommendations often became the rules he had to enforce.

He progressed from the physician everyone loved and admired to the chief responsible for decision making in a very crucial time for medicine. He kept his characteristics as a unique and beloved person and a fine and confident surgeon, but his first responsibility, he felt, was always for humans in distress—not just patients and colleagues but everyone serving the public. When AirCare helicopters had fatal crashes, he led others to join in efforts to bring the Medical Center family together and remember those who died in service. He became for many a visible rock of security. He pursued objectives in a way so that the public did not lose sight that this is a Christian complex still adhering to its historic premise to heal the sick and serve the desperate.

And for many he became an invisible promoter for his colleagues. His desire was simple: Help them become their very best and get them where they need to be as chosen instruments in medicine. Because of this single trait, he became a mentor for many.

As he increased his CPS duties on behalf of patients and staff, his demeanor often seemed brusque—because his time for self-denying service was consuming his energy—and so his conversations were reduced to essentials. As chief, he was a plain spokesman, not talkative—unless teaching students in class or surgery. However, he easily entered into conversations when someone had needs or wanted to talk about bears and fishing, Christ and John the Baptist, or using the mind for pondering a matter. He looks like Spencer Tracy and has his same droll-like personality. He often is called a bear-of-a-man—big in love, incisive in decisions, reliable as daybreak.

His was the greatest era of change thus far in the Medical Center's history.

His colleagues, without hesitation, credit him for helping to facilitate many of the changes needed to keep the institution on its road toward exceptional quality and superior accreditation.

The degree of distinctiveness with which the Medical Center entered this new century came in large part because here again he wanted his institutions to become their very best: chosen instruments of restoration for people in times of medical dysfunction.

In his role as surgeon and professor, he wanted the same for his students. They respected his surgical skill and teaching acuity. He became their inspiration in a time when physicians felt less revered. He exhibited a trait that said titles would not get the job done unless performed with perceivable talents and unselfish motives.

Pennell, colleagues say, "is a symbol of what we want our institutions to be, and if these institutions are to function properly, they must have a system focused on excellence in all respects, and a CPS leader like Tim Pennell to handle the monumental changes now so prevalent daily in medicine."

All of the chiefs have been appropriate for their seasons of service. Their contributions have been remarkable. Their common quality has been their legendary fidelity.

Without the ardent dedication and gratuity from hundreds of service-givers over the years—not just the chiefs and the executives—this Medical Center could not have achieved the magnificence it so enjoys today.

III THE AWESOMENESS OF HEALTH CARE

The medical school faculty can elect only one of its colleagues to be its representative on the executive committee of the Chief of Professional Services.

So when the faculty chose Pennell in 1981, it was an expression of approval.

When the leaders of the medical school and hospital chose him as chief in 1986, it was acknowledgment of his readiness.

He is the only chief to enter this continuum with service on the executive committee and the only graduate of Wake Forest University School of Medicine ever to hold this position.

His was a season of difficult and persistent problems—and opportunities.

He and the Office for Chief of Professional Services confronted an ongoing calamitous issue: human immunodeficiency virus (HIV) that causes acquired immune deficiency syndrome (AIDS), the broader issue of infectious diseases, and the need for a clean blood supply. These issues still need CPS's continuum of surveillance.

In 1981, physicians in America began to encounter a virus causing HIV/AIDS that would change forever the way they would practice medicine and prevention.

AIDS first appeared in the United States in California in unusual forms of pneumonia and then rare skin cancers, basically among homosexual men. Within a year, the disease moved east across the country and into the lives of heterosexual men and women and their children, leaving them with vulnerable immune systems, deadly viruses that would cut short their lives, and other deadly infections and cancers.

The virus enters the bloodstream through blood and body secretions, unsanitary intravenous drug abuse, unprotected sex, recurring infections, and untested transfusions, all attacking the very immune system cells needed to destroy the infectious disease.

HIV/AIDS was challenging medicine and the Medical Center was not immune.

In 1982, while Pennell was on the executive committee, CPS realized that the Medical Center—and the rest of the world including

Forsyth County—was facing a pandemic disease whose cause was not fully known or understood.

By 1986, when Pennell became chief, he became aware further of the serious implications of HIV/AIDS. Today it is ranked as medicine's worst epidemic.

Thousands of AIDS cases began to be diagnosed in the United States. The disease's spread became rampant. The government was criticized for not putting into effect preventative measures to halt this medical catastrophe. No curative drugs were known. But evidence of AIDS' presence was visible and persistent.

The disease spawned a second epidemic: fear. Symptoms, on average, can take 10 years to appear. Victims often face the dreaded disease without support from family, friends, or health providers. They suffer from the impediments of shame, denial, stigma, fear, equal employment and housing opportunities, and eligibility for health coverage.

"When AIDS was first recognized as a significant problem," Pennell explained, "this institution and this faculty and the employees went through every reaction that the general public had, including, 'This illness is prevalent because of sin and this is God's punishment. These people should be isolated like lepers. We should refuse to treat them. They all should have a scarlet letter 'A' tattooed on their forehead or their chest!'

"There was a proposal—only a proposal—that signs be put at every hospital entrance saying, 'If you come here to get treatment, you are going to be tested for AIDS.'

"And we went through a period in which every patient with a blood-borne pathogen—basically AIDS and hepatitis—had a card on the door designating the disease and stating precautions for the caregivers." AIDS patients struck back, citing the cards as discriminative.

These cards eventually were removed but not without opposition from the surgical faculty that asked CPS to make known all infectious diseases either by notation on patients' records or by precautionary signs in the rooms or above the beds. The surgeons emphasized their continued willingness to deliver full care to AIDS patients, but they felt they and all caregivers were facing an occupational hazard by not knowing what type of infection was involved. If the patient was known to be HIV positive, they argued, precautions could be intensified.

The physicians also expressed concern that infectious patients were being placed in semiprivate rooms with fresh postoperative surgical patients, thus possibly compromising medical health safety. They called for better room occupancy planning, which was set into motion immediately.

AIDS, Pennell said, "is still an emotional issue and now 21 years later it is still being dealt with here." When AIDS first emerged in this country, he explained, it was the first major fatal illness medicine had encountered in decades, and there was no surefire treatment for it. Because of its complications, he added, HIV/AIDS infections today remain a public health threat.

To further complicate the issue, the diagnosis was kept confidential—even to the health care workers on the case. This caused anger among caregivers. They felt patients' mental well-being came before their physical survival.

CPS solved that problem in 1988, Pennell said, by following infection-control measures set up by the federally operated Centers for Disease Control (CDC), "the first to develop and put forth this concept." The federal Occupational Safety and Health Administration (OSHA), in response to the public's concern over exposure to AIDS and Hepatitis B and C, mandated these precautions in 1991. Guidelines also were developed for fire service personnel, emergency medical technicians, paramedics, and law enforcement and correctional facility personnel.

The standards required that all health care workers who might come into contact with blood and body fluids in the workplace be educated in infection control. The basic precautions included using surgical or examination gloves made of vinyl or latex for all patient contact, changing gloves between patients, washing hands thoroughly after removing gloves, wearing water-repellent gowns and protective masks or glasses, and continuing waste management safety procedures.

Secondary precautions included prevention of injuries from needle sticks, scalpel blades, and other sharp instruments or devices used during medical procedures; proper disposal or disinfection of these items following use; and blood-spill cleanups with household bleach while wearing gloves.

Pennell, as well as others, personally went further. He began to educate people outside the Medical Center about the virus, particularly when he worked at the local Reynolds Health Center and Crisis Control Ministry or during overseas mission trips, trying to correct false fears about its transmission. At that time many people thought the disease was airborne and could be transmitted merely by touching an AIDS patient.

Pennell wanted no one to die from the disease because of ignorance, fear, or insufficient treatment.

CPS recognized that the mission of the hospital is to provide care, reduce suffering, and to prevent or deal with the presence of disease and injury. The social and moral issues involved around AIDS affected that mission. The urgent need for a hospital epidemiologist became evident to CPS in 1986, as did the need in 1987 for an HIV coordinator to develop reeducational programs for physicians and employees working with body fluids. Both appointments were made and the offices are still in operation.

Known HIV-positive patients were a risk but greater were the risks from virus-infected patients who did not disclose their illnesses.

CPS had to decide if all patients on blood and body fluids needed to be treated as if they had AIDS, if all patients admitted with a suspected HIV virus should be handled with precaution, or even if every patient admitted needed to be tested for the virus.

And legally, should patients with AIDS receive more confidentiality than other patients? A North Carolina statute was passed requiring that the identity of the patient be kept strictly confidential, except in court order cases. But details of the virus could be used for statistical purposes.

Pennell said the universal precaution concept is simple: "Protect yourself from AIDS by protecting yourself from every patient—everyone—not just the ones you know have it."

CPS further enlarged its medical policies by preparing an employee manual outlining infection control programs for treatment, precautions, and isolation for all patients with AIDS, Hepatitis B and C, chickenpox/herpes zoster, herpes simplex, influenza, measles, mumps, polio, rubella, syphilis, tuberculosis, and methicillin-resistant staphylococcus aureus or staph.

Putting universal precautions into effect, Pennell explained, "was unbelievably costly." Every time doctors, nurses, housekeepers, assistants, or employees touched anything having to do with infected patients, they had to be protected at least with gloves and often with masks. "It became a huge, huge, *huge* expense for the hospital."

The cost increased in operating rooms, emergency rooms, dental offices, and pathology laboratories, for there the risks are greater because of invasive procedures and exposure to body fluids. When the medical staff works with cuts or jagged bones, injects needles or inserts wires, or removes or implants appliances, they must massively protect themselves, Pennell explained.

The epidemic caused medicine to recognize that optimal precautions must remain an everyday, every patient safeguard.

In 1986, the hospital implemented the "look-back program." Pennell identified it as "one of the bad dilemmas" that CPS had to deal with at that time: identifying patients "who had received transfusions when the screening was not as sophisticated as it became later. That was the big struggle. Do you or don't you go back and tell these patients that in prior years—nine or 10 years before—the blood they received had not been tested for the AIDS virus or had tested positively for the virus? Do you send out that fear?

"Yes, you tell them," he answered. Letters were sent to these patients explaining the problem, knowing it would cause negative publicity for the hospital—and for all health care institutions in the nation—who got blood products from the then major source, the American Red Cross.

The Red Cross initiated the look-back procedure when it discovered years later through retesting that some blood donations were contaminated with the AIDS infection.

CPS and the Red Cross advised patients to avail themselves of medical follow-up either at the hospital or at a care institution of their choice. It turned out for Baptist Hospital that its near-dozen units of blood under question were at extremely low risk. Of the 180 patients identified as needing follow-up therapy, 30 were still alive and the hospital monitored by letter their need for retesting and counseling.

While no cure could be offered to these patients, there was the need to educate both patients and their physicians about the virus and subsequent precautions.

Later CPS set up a look-back advisory committee to monitor the purity of the hospital's own blood bank collection. It continues today, for all medical institutions still face the possibility of their staff being infected while transferring blood components.

"Do you ask patients to submit to blood tests to see if they have AIDS?" Pennell asked. "They can refuse. I can't force them to let me draw blood, whether it is to test for infections, blood sugar, or blood alcohol, unless they agree. Just like I can't force them to get treatment for AIDS."

Should employees report that they were stuck by a needle while giving medications, "then we go to the patients and say, 'It would help us tremendously to know what your AIDS status is.' Most patients will agree with that, but there are those who won't. It may be that they know they have the virus, but they don't want to document it for personal, family, employment, and insurance reasons. So CPS continues to deal with these problems of AIDS."

Pennell said protecting patients and employees continues to be very expensive. Medical Center policy regulations require that all new employees be tested for infections, all accidents dealing with body fluids and injections be reported and followed up, and all patient and treatment rooms be equipped with protective gloves and masks. "Protection was something we had to fight for at length—and still do."

Universal precautions are "an aggravation for everybody, particularly when people don't fully understand what is going on." If precautionary regulations are not followed, individuals working within the Medical Center receive warnings. Their continued abuse can lead to disciplinary measures.

"If patients are immunocompromised," Pennell said, "then you put them in isolation—not for segregation but for their own protection. Most don't object to this—if they are intelligent."

Today all health care institutions and blood banks are under federal mandate to test all blood donors and donations to detect the possible presence of HIV antibodies, hepatitis B and C, syphilis, and other viruses. Because the tests cannot be 100 percent accurate, potential donors are asked in the screening process about possible risk factors connected to these infections. As a further precaution, each donation is tested before being made available for transfusions.

In 1987, AZT became one of the first anti-HIV drugs available in America. It alone was not enough. It often did slow the virus' progress to full-blown AIDS, especially from mother to baby, but it took another decade before doctors had a therapy potent enough to rein in, but not cure, AIDS. One of the best treatments still is a drug cocktail with protease inhibitors used in conjunction with pills taken at specific times during the day.

New drug combinations stopped some healthy people who were HIV infected from getting sicker. The rate of new cases began to slow, as did the number of deaths.

For others, the news was not as hopeful, for the virus with its thousands of strains can develop resistance to drugs. And anti-HIV treatment in America can reach up to $15,000 a year per patient, often making it impossible for the uninsured and impoverished to receive health care.

At this time researchers realize there is no known safe HIV level in the blood, for caretakers are unable to totally cure hidden dormant virus pockets, known as CD4 cells, smoldering within the body. These latent viral reservoirs form soon after people are infected. Thus, the only promise of complete worldwide AIDS eradication will come when a new vaccine or drug can totally strangle the virus. Until then, physicians advocate immediate preventive measures, therapy, and disclosure to partners.

Here in the new century, the AIDS virus is still one of the major biomedical challenges, Pennell said, but thankfully American researchers are leading in the drive for a scientific breakthrough to halt or totally control this disease that can affect anyone.

CDC reported in June 2002 that about 900,000 people now living in the United States are infected with HIV; approximately 40,000 new infections occur every year in America; and the majority of the newly infected are males. Of the recorded new cases, CDC estimates that close to half, 42 percent, are men having sex with men (MSM), followed by heterosexual men and women infected through sex, 33 percent, and 25 percent through substance abuse, such as using dirty syringes or trading sex for drugs.

An alarming number of young people worldwide, ages 15 to 24, are infected. They are neither aware of how the disease is spread nor how to protect themselves. In the United States, these youths are too young to remember the start of the epidemic, and they live under the apathy that a cure-all vaccine will be available soon to save them, so the virus infection no longer seems serious to them.

Since the epidemic began, CDC added, 448,060 Americans are believed to have died of HIV/AIDS-related causes as of December 2000. Accurate numbers are unknown, as there is no universal data collection system in use in America.

Currently, CDC said, 40 million people worldwide are estimated to be living with HIV, less than 2 percent are receiving treatment, and nearly half are women living in underdeveloped countries. And over 40 percent of HIV-positive Americans do not know they are infected until they develop AIDS. This means they have missed out on a decade or more of treatment and possibly transmitted the disease to others. Many still are not getting treatment, either out of fear or poor access to quality medical care.

A high percentage of Americans newly infected with HIV, CDC found, are blacks and about half of them are females. Thus CDC has renewed educational treatment programs for those not practicing safe sex or safe IV drug use.

Like CDC, Pennell said, WFUBMC is also intensifying its HIV and substance abuse prevention and treatment services and advocating better integration of early medical intervention for *all* infectious diseases, including syphilis and gonorrhea.

Of the Americans who have died of HIV-AIDS, 6,676 of them lived in North Carolina. AIDS became reportable by name in North Carolina in 1984 and HIV infection in 1990. From the early 1980s through December 31, 2001, the North Carolina Department of Health and Human Services (NCDHH) documented 20,525 first-time reported HIV cases. While the number of cases was highest from 1992-1995, there is now evidence from HIV-disease reports that new cases have become relatively stable since 1996. As of December 2000, the number of people in the state living with HIV is about 68 percent males and about 31 percent females. In this group, NCDHH reports, nearly 24 percent are white non-Hispanics and 72 percent are blacks/African Americans or non-Hispanics. The highest group, over 38 percent, are those 30 to 39 years old, also the nation's highest age bracket for people living with HIV/AIDS. In its first-quarter 2002 report, the state health department predicts that the HIV epidemic will continue to invade both urban and rural areas; that MSM cases will account for a significant proportion of new infection reports, particularly among men of color; that heterosexual transmission of HIV will continue to increase, especially among blacks; that the rate of infections will continue to grow among women in heterosexual contacts; and that minorities will continue to be disproportionately affected in all risk groups.

CDC has identified Forsyth County as a growing area of virus-carrying individuals. It also notes that most of the new cases, here and across the nation, are among minorities. The state health department is predicting an increasing number of cases from Hispanics due to their rapid presence in the state. And it notes that the epidemic, once considered an urban disease, is now reaching rural areas, including Forsyth County, which has an elevation in HIV/AIDS cases.

Disturbed by the increase of new infections, CDC is questioning if the powerful drugs are losing their potential to hold off death, but the reason may be more personal. Some with AIDS, who now experience a fuller and longer life under the latest drug therapies, may feel the virus is a manageable chronic condition, so they are taking a chance and reverting to high-risk behaviors that led initially to their infections.

The Medical Center, Pennell explained, must continue to monitor in-place prevention standards and pursue barrier-protection measures against *all* infectious diseases—all under CPS's jurisdiction.

Because of the growing population of these patients, he said the Medical Center added a special infection clinic, employed medical staff with special expertise in epidemiology, and enlarged its research.

Pennell noted that researchers at the Medical Center "have been on the forefront of every new drug trial since AZT was first produced" and that pursuit for control still remains a working goal for them.

The race for an effective vaccine that controls or cures has geared up, Pennell said, but none is in sight. Knowledge about AIDS/HIV and drug addiction and their preventative measures are still the most effective means to stop the global epidemic now into its third decade.

Worldwide health care organizations have issued a plea that any vaccines or cures developed be made available first to people who need them the most—mainly the poor and impoverished, especially those in Africa, Eastern Europe, China, India, Indonesia, and the Caribbean.

IV MEDICINE'S GOAL IS HEALTH CORRECTION

Correction of poor health is a goal of medicine. However, it is not always a possibility. But when it is a probability and errors are made, the goal is thwarted.

When it is an impossibility, the goal is to be a comforter.

During Pennell's time as chief, the Medical Center became further acquainted with these two objectives.

A national research group reported near the end of 1999 on what had been a fact often kept silent: High rates of medical mistakes were causing excessive deaths, disabilities, and suffering throughout the nation's health care institutions.

The Institute of Medicine, a division of the National Academy of Sciences, reported that medical faults by health care providers kill between 44,000 to 98,000 hospitalized people each year and they were the eighth leading cause of death, ahead of AIDS, highway accidents, heart attacks, and breast cancer. This report later was defined as an overexaggeration.

The stated reasons for medical mistakes? Human errors, bad judgment calls, chronic fatigue due to excessively long work hours, incorrect drug dosages, failure of medical devices or their incorrect use, outdated medical systems and procedures to store medical data, and poor handwriting. The latter often leaves pharmacists and health caretakers unable to decipher and dispense correct medications and treatments.

"First, do no harm" is a vanguard pledge of uppermost importance to doctors and hospitals, for they do not wish their care to spawn impairments. Today's physicians are overtaxed by excessive patient data collection demanded by insurance providers and health care overseers, so handwriting of even the most meticulous doctor can appear harried.

Then there is the problem of drugs with look- and sound-alike names and misunderstood dosage amounts. It is ever difficult for health care workers these days to keep up with the ever-changing scientific advancements in medications and their hazards.

But now physicians can use hand-held computer devices to process prescriptions electronically, ending queries about handwriting, dosage amounts, and drug names. Some machines even determine if the patient's insurance plan covers the medication and what might be a less costly choice.

As health care institutions move deeper into computerized record keeping—and Baptist Hospital has—fewer mistakes are expected, for computer programs now check doctors' orders against patients' medical histories. And physicians and other caregivers are resorting to on-the-spot computer and recorder documentation of medical data.

Patients also are responsible for medical mistakes, for treatments can go awry if they don't divulge medications being taken, if they don't take prescriptions correctly, if they don't report being allergic to certain drugs, or if they don't divulge their complete medical history.

If treatments are stopped early or invalid medicinal substitutes are used, then patients can compromise their own health. Foul-ups can occur, too, if patients do not tell medical—or emergency room—practitioners *every* medication they are taking, including alternative and herbal formulas and nonprescription remedies.

Medical insurers also are part of the risk factor when they cut corners by forcing hospital discharges prematurely to save money or when they don't allow doctors to prescribe needed high-quality health care procedures. Many patients feel their insurance providers are pressuring physicians to spend less time with them, but this is not necessarily true.

Immediately after the Institute released its report, Pennell, as Baptist Hospital's CPS, issued a statement to ease any unreasonable fear or misunderstanding:

"Human error can never be eliminated from any human system, especially one as complex as medical care. But we have tried to devise a system of oversight that will keep errors at a minimum. We also have tried to create an environment in which new ideas about improving the system are always welcome."

Two years previously, he continued, the hospital pharmacy installed "a robotic drug-dispensing system. This is a special centralized drug distribution method that automates the storage, retrieval, and dispensing of pharmaceuticals. This system has dramatically improved accuracy and efficiency. And it has freed pharmacists to spend more time with physicians and patients to assure safe and appropriate use of drugs" and to explain drug interactions, effectiveness, and benefits.

The robot is given patients' diagnoses and information on other medications being taken, so if there are any questions by either the robot, the physician, or nurse, the written prescription can be reconfirmed to ensure patient safety.

To alleviate further concern, Baptist Hospital is now implementing a computerized prescription order system to avoid problems sometimes encountered with handwriting, an item mentioned in the Institute report, and to catch ill-suited prescriptions that could endanger patients.

Another grievous goof specified by the Institute was wrong-side surgery.

Baptist Hospital "some time ago implemented a correct-side procedure," Pennell said. "The patient, while still awake, confirms the exact location of the body part to be operated on and while in the surgical holding room watches as the nurse puts a mark to indicate the patient confirms the location.

"Our incidents of wrong-side surgery are exceedingly low. At no time ever has an amputation or anything catastrophic like that taken place here. There have been maybe three wrong preparatory skin incisions made in a five-year period out of the many, many thousands of surgical patients, but never has the wrong breast been removed, never has the wrong extremity been amputated, or anything like that.

"I am pleased with what this institution has done and is doing" to cut back on possible medical errors, "and I think we are way ahead in the broad category of built-in safeguards. Over 15 years ago we went to standardized anesthesia equipment" and procedures, making that field of surgery even safer.

"Now does this mean that on occasion we make mistakes? Yes, we do, and as long as there is a human element involved in this, there will be an occasional error. But the bottom line is this: I think this institution has taken every measure it can—in every way now known—to safeguard and protect its patients. And in this, I think, we are way, way, *way* ahead of most health care institutions. Patients coming here must know that we are a 'safe' hospital."

But it must be remembered that even in medicine today, with its high level of success, unpredictable complications can occur, for neither physicians, nurses, or anesthesiologists can be sure totally how patients will react to surgical and drug interventions.

The Institute called on Congress to establish a new federal patient-safety agency to reduce in half by 2002 those errors caused by treatment or diagnostic procedural errors. It asked Congress to require all health care providers to voluntarily report to state governments any medical errors that caused patients adverse harm or death.[5]

The Institute panel noted that names of physicians reporting errors should be protected because of confidentiality and liability laws.

The report also suggested that licensing and regulatory agencies

[5] The National Academy of Sciences has no power currently to enforce its suggestions.

should monitor health care institutions reporting violations and regularly reexamine their competency.

Should a preventable fault occur, Pennell said, the hospital has an *internal* process for handling it through "fair-hearing grievance" procedures. "We participate in a national, voluntary, private agency to which we report any grievances. If we have a catastrophic event with a certain drug or a certain piece of equipment, it is reported. The agency shares this with participating hospitals so that the mistake will not be repeated.

"I think this institution is very, very conscientious in trying to detect, deal with, and prevent any errors we encounter, be it wrong medication, wrong dosage, or wrong-side surgery. This is one of the thrusts of the hospital's risk management program. If we are wrong or it is alleged we are wrong, what can we do to correct this? What did we learn from the event? What can we do to prevent it from happening again? Or, if we weren't wrong, how can we clear that perception?

"I don't think we have difficulty getting physicians or health care workers to acknowledge a wrong. There are many situations in which they on their own call risk management to say, 'I think I may have made an error.' Under our system, errors—and even close calls—can be reported without fear, and once their causes are known, the likelihood of repetition is reduced."

The practice and delivery of medical care, Pennell explained, "is a daily learning process. What we could not cure yesterday may be easily cured today because medicine is an epic tale of success and failure. Sometimes we may stumble, but always we must learn. In this learning, we demonstrate our willingness to change, modify, and reexamine the many facets in the practice of modern-day medicine.

"This philosophy of continuum improvement," Pennell added, "is best accomplished in a blame-free, process-focused environment in which we evaluate all that we do to determine if we can improve.

"We must see the patient as central in our ongoing learning, and we must be open and honest with our successes and shortcomings in this very human process we call health care. We at this Medical Center strive to fulfill our obligations and responsibilities to our patients and their families and to the improvement of the evolving practice of medicine. And CPS leads us in this process."

All medical specialty boards in the nation require all specialists—pediatricians, neurologists, surgeons, et cetera—to be recertified every 10 years, Pennell said. But at Baptist Hospital "we go beyond that safeguard and reexamine all of our physicians *internally* on an *annual* basis to ensure that they are competent" and that all credentials are up-to-date. This is a part of CPS's supervisory duties: to monitor doctors' competency, records of disciplinary history, professional misconduct, or license violations.

Should a physician, nurse, researcher, health care provider, house-keeper, dietitian, or therapist continue over and over again to make miscalculations, Pennell said, then punitive measures are taken, "including termination, loss of privileges, probation, strict guidelines under which he or she can or cannot work with or without supervision. There are a number of corrective and protective measures possible" under CPS's direction.

The Joint Commission on Accreditation of Healthcare Organizations (JCAHO), which sanctions 80 percent of the nation's hospitals, Pennell explained, "would like for us to report any medical errors to them, but most medical institutions do not. The route we have elected to go is the private agency, which gathers all of the information about a catastrophic event—without disclosing the name of the institution or without breaking confidentially—and shares it with other participating institutions so that they, too, can learn from others' problems.

"JCAHO in our 1999 accrediting review asked if we had had any catastrophic events and how we elected to handle them. We gave them our answers and they were totally acceptable. Accreditation has never been penalized here for medical errors."

JCAHO set up a requirement in 1998 that all hospitals establish a process for reviewing and reporting sentinel events. And Baptist Hospital immediately complied.

Sentinel events are those resulting in an unanticipated death or major permanent loss of limb or function not related to the natural course of patients' illnesses or underlying conditions or to a visitor while within the hospital complex. Such events include suicide of patients under around-the-clock care in a hospital residential treatment center or crisis stabilization center; infant abduction or discharge to the wrong family; rape; hemolytic transfusion reaction because of incompatibility of blood products; inability to wipe out hospital-acquired antibiotic-resistant staph infections; and surgery on wrong patients or wrong body parts.

These steps for reducing medical errors are consistent with the hospital's 1999 stated mission of providing comprehensive health care services of the highest quality. Other resolves are: maintaining advanced clinical standards in research and educational programs, sharing knowledge and expertise, giving excellent health care in a caring and compassionate manner consistent with its Judeo-Christian heritage, and surpassing professional quality standards to meet the highest expectations of those it serves.

The interpretation of all these objectives is the responsibility of the Office for Chief of Professional Services and the hospital trustees, according to guidelines outlined in the initial 1977 Patients' Bill of Rights. In its 1993 Quality Improvement Plan, the hospital pledged to continue improving all aspects of patient care, within available resources, to achieve maximal clinical outcomes and high patient satisfaction, and to resolve all identified problems.

The hospital's medical staff abides by these precepts. These physicians are from the medical school faculty; however, all faculty members do not have hospital privileges as admitting and practicing physicians and dentists. Those approved are subject to ongoing review and evaluation of professional competency and valid current licensing.

In addition to being able to work with others and with patients, medical staff physicians are obligated to abide by professional standards, ethics, and policies. CPS ensures under stipulations of appointment that these physicians have no conditions, such as alcohol or drug use, that would impair their practice. They also are required not to discriminate against those with whom they work because of their sex, race, creed, national origin, age, or disabilities. Appointments are made on a two-year basis.

The active full-time medical staff admits patients to Baptist Hospital and, where appropriate, assumes emergency service care and consulting assignments.

Corrective actions are part of the medical staff bylaws and rules, reviewed and updated, as needed, annually. If the conduct of practitioners is considered to be lower than stated standards, then the CPS executive committee reviews these incidents.

Corrective actions range from letters of warning, admonition, or reprimand. Recommendations vary from reduction, suspension, or revocation of clinical privileges. All actions and decisions are conducted on legal principles.

In addition to overseeing the practice, performance, and credentials of the medical staff, CPS is the intermediary between the hospital and medical school in all matters concerning all professional services provided for patients. This involves practitioners from the medical school's 29 academic departments.

Another CPS duty is to supervise the hospital's house staff. The primary function of these licensed residents and postdoctoral students is to continue the study and practice of medicine as designated and supervised by the medical staff. Medical students also work in the hospital under the close supervision of residents and attending medical staff.

Maintaining patients' medical records is a major responsibility for these three ranks of practitioners. Records include personal and legal information as well as medical histories, diagnoses, reasons for admission or treatment, and diagnostic, pharmaceutical, and therapeutic orders. Other assessments are made as patients progress through the clinical examination process.

One of CPS's major functions is to see that medical records are kept up-to-date, confidential, and complete. This means that verbal orders, operative notes, histories, and physical exam summaries must be written and signed by physicians within 24 hours. Progress notes must be signed every three days and discharge notes and orders must be signed by the day patients leave the hospital. Over the years, this obligation has been fraught with problems, for busy physicians with high volumes of patients must contend with high volumes of paperwork. So physicians must decide which comes first: patient care or documentation.

Over time, CPS set up guidelines to correct this record-keeping problem. When adherence became lax, censure measures were added.

The hospital started converting to computerized patient records in 1994. This centralized online and on-demand system enhances all clinical practice, research, education, and managed care information. Caretakers now have direct access at the point of care where they can more easily make additions while data is fresh in their minds. It also provides nurses with easier reexamination of orders to be implemented and access to documents regarding patients' desires for a natural death.

The hospital's policy on patients' rights to "a peaceful and dignified death" was updated in 1999 and approved by Pennell and Preslar and confirmed by hospital trustees. Prepared by the Medical Center Ethics Committee, it includes policies for implementing patients' wishes and for withholding or withdrawing therapies.

So it is the Office for Chief of Professional Services that shepherds the care not only of the hospital's medical staff but also those it serves. Much of CPS's time is spent in executing the fine details needed for medical safety, patient protection, and perpetual patient well-being as defined by medical, moral, legal, and ethical principles.

The role of comforter is another area where mistakes cannot be made.

Patient health directives are sad but necessary procedures for CPS to outline and for physicians and caregivers to follow.

The hospital's current patient self-determination policy reflects its key values of compassion and integrity. It gives patients opportunities to express their own wishes regarding their medical safekeeping, including the right to accept or refuse medical care, mental health or surgical treatment, and the right to formulate advance directives.

The care the hospital provides, however, is not conditioned on whether or not patients have advance directives in their files. Pennell explained the hospital's policy regarding precise procedures for implementing these directions. It is a medical difficulty that cannot be shunned, for death is a given that all will encounter.

One directive concerns withholding or withdrawal of life-giving procedures. To initiate this policy, the physician makes decisions based on a patient's advanced directive and his or her present condition, which are then noted on the medical record. The physician may decide to write the withholding or withdrawal order only after agreement has been obtained verbally from a competent patient. If the patient is incompetent, the physician's decisions are based on the presence of a health care power of attorney or a living will. Should neither document be on file, the physician seeks guidance from the patient's guardian, spouse, parents (of a minor), or the majority of relatives of the first degree. This is especially true when the patient's condition is terminal, incurable, or in a persistent vegetative state.

When none of these procedures can be followed, the attending physician may write the orders only if a second physician concurs. Included under this hospital policy is the procedure for implementing a "do not resuscitate" (DNR) order requested by the patient. It means that a patient's needs and interests should be considered before the family's.

While patients' rights are recognized, the hospital and its medical staff remain "committed first to the preservation of life, the alleviation of suffering, and promotion of health" for their patients, Pennell said.

Under DNR orders—so prevalent in today's hospitals—no further therapeutic or resuscitative efforts are invoked; rather, the medical staff and the omnipresent nursing providers move to palliative care. The intent then is to provide patients with comfort and presence as they near the end of life. Patients often fear the atmosphere of death more than the act, for they do not wish to suffer needless pain or prolonged agony due to machine-sustained life or aggressive therapies, Pennell said. With advance directives in place, he added, patients can control, rightly or wrongly, their final state of existence—even over family members unwilling to accept that further medical intervention is futile.

It is difficult for professional caregivers to give up, for the premise of their lives and the reason for their education is to heal, to deter the failure of health.

But then life, too, has its seasons.

V New Century Haunted
By Old Century Needs

The human face that knows no season in the continuum of daily hospital bedside care, hour by hour, is that of the nurse.

She—and increasingly also he—is ever available at hospital beds, in intensive care units, special recovery units, and outpatient therapy programs. Because of her role, she is more perdurably involved with the patients' treatment, medications, and comfort because she is the one who usually performs these basics as part of her watchkeeper role.

CPS's watchkeeper role on behalf of nurses is to make sure that they are neither overworked, understaffed, inadequately educated nor underpaid. It is a protectorship that all chiefs have assumed, for without nurses the totality of healing could not be performed. Medicine would have a stroke without its nursing staff. And patient care would be crippled.

During Pennell's watch, the nursing shortages rose acutely again— as it did across the nation. And he sees the problem becoming catastrophic in the coming years when fewer nurses may be available unless the condition can be corrected. It is an issue that CPS constantly appraises.

"It will not be as easy to recover from as the last shortage" in the late 1980s or even the one in the late 1970s, Pennell believes. "Shortages come and go in cycles and unfortunately they seem to get worse with each new cycle."

Now that Baptist Hospital is no longer running its own nursing school, it has renewed its recruitment strategies, offered a tuition reimbursement program, increased salaries and sign-on bonuses, expanded time off, and added benefits to stabilize its supply of nurses and assisting health care workers.

During the nursing deficit of the 1980s, Pennell recalled, Baptist and Forsyth Memorial Hospital "started the CODE BLUE program to interest people in nursing, made scholarships available, and found young women and some men to go to Forsyth Technical Community College and Winston-Salem State University" for education in nursing-related professions. The hospitals then paid for the education with the

33

understanding that the students would come to work for them after graduation.

At that time, Pennell said, "the greatest majority of these students were from the black community. These were people who wanted to be more than cigarette sellers or checkout clerks—and I am not putting down those categories. These were people who wanted a profession.

"Fewer and fewer people are going into nursing because it is hard, hard, *hard* work. It is demanding, particularly hospital inpatient nursing, especially intensive and emergency care. There are huge responsibilities, health risks, and less free time. Many today look upon nursing as being less prestigious. It is losing its glamour and its glory."

It is necessary continuously for nurses to adjust to new treatments, drugs, and technology; confront burnout; and gain academic degrees to feel equal to their co-workers.

And now there are more opportunities and better paying jobs for nurses in private clinics, HMOs and pharmaceutical companies, and in other careers, such as those in computer industries.

While nurses love their work, they are being overwhelmed and stressed out by bigger workloads, sicker patients, more documentation, and less respect, so increasingly they are not recommending nursing as a career.

"Nursing is really suffering and it is going to get worse," Pennell lamented. "It will be one of the first major catastrophes in this new century, coming near when the first decade is half over"—now predicted around the year 2007 as the baby boomers, including nurses, retire. The average age of today's registered nurses is 46, and only 10 percent are under 30.

"I think this next go-round the nurses are going to come from rural Northwest North Carolina and the Hispanic community. There are a lot of very bright and very capable young women and young men in the Hispanic community—they are a growing percent of our community's population—and I think they can and will make excellent nurses given the opportunity."

In its effort to further upgrade the nursing vocation, Pennell believes CPS eventually will adopt a professional designation of "clinical nurse coordinator." He defined this "as an individual who will still practice under the supervision of a physician," but the designation will better define the "whole role of nursing specialists which is changing so radically."

When the Medical Center enters new or extended services, Pennell said, it not only must entice physician specialists to its staff but also nurse practitioners, for the technological phases of medicine are ever developing, especially at the patient level. Nurses must be qualified to interpret these radical developments in health therapies and execute these medical interventions as needed.

In today's health care systems, Pennell said, medical restoration is being fought not only in hospitals but also in nursing homes and home health care agencies, so even more adept nurses are needed to backup doctors and their assistants in their watch to help patients recover. And yet in the past six years, there has been a 25 percent decline in those graduating from nursing programs and taking board exams.

In the late 1980s, Baptist Hospital and CPS started earnestly again to look for ways to get some responsibilities off of nurses so that they would have more time to care for their patients. In the late 1990s, and continuing today, nurses complain like physicians that paperwork is taking more and more of their time, preventing their traditional role of hands-on care with patients. Increasingly this major record-keeping function is being passed on to aides who input this data into patients' computer-captured records.

"There are many, many things in health care delivery today," Pennell said, "that nurses can do far better than I can. I'll be the first to acknowledge and recognize that. It is essential—and it always has been true—that we work collaboratively and decide who can best handle the totality of patient care without trying to knock, suppress, abuse, or degrade either profession."

Because it is a constant obligation for the hospital to maintain an adequate nurse-to-patient ratio, CPS finds it necessary to look at ways hospital medical procedures are conducted, for the nursing shortage is not subsiding.

Should CPS close some of its available beds because of a nursing staff shortage, it would mean that patients in intensive care units, for example, would be retained there longer rather than being transferred to less acute units and thus preventing room availability for fewer new patients. It also would mean that these specialized nurses would be overworked caring for the overload. This would contribute further to poor morale, fatigue and stress, and staff turnover.

CPS adopted a short-term solution in the late 1980s by employing traveling nurses, pharmacists, and respiratory therapists from outside the area who float from hospital to hospital, wherever needed. This practice has become a permanent answer, for the shortage is approaching yet another severe crisis. Usually these nomadic workers sign on for at least a 13-week commitment.

In 2002,when its nurse vacancy rate was 4.5 percent, Baptist went out of the country for help, finding an answer in the Philippines where nurses are unable to find work or earn livable wages. Baptist also learned that the Filipino nurses wanted to come to the United States. Upon arrival, they have to pass licensing exams and meet immigration requirements, but waiting for them are sign-on bonuses, housing opportunities, and refund of airfare and legal fees.

Hospital management continues to review what nurses are doing, what is required of them by law, and what tasks they perform that others could be hired to do. The hospital recognizes that it has to offer nurses more than inducements to join its staff. It has to give nurses opportunities for specialized training in new medical procedures. It has to provide nurses with vertical mobility so that they can climb the career ladder. It has to revamp work schedules so that nurses have more time for a personal life.

There is a trend today, Pennell said, for nurses and some health care technicians, such as pharmacists, "to work 12-hour shifts for four days and then have three to four days off, whereas they used to work eight hours a day and get one day off every two weeks." Then there are programs at Baptist where part of the nursing staff works only on weekends, putting in 12 to 14 hours a day on Saturdays and Sundays. A lot of nurses like this flexible scheduling, especially working mothers, Pennell explained. While they work weekends, their spouses are at home with the children. This way both parents have time with the children and they avoid day care.

Hospitals like Baptist, however, do develop on-site day care centers to serve their health care staff, making available safe learning environments for children and easy access visits for their on-duty parents.

The hospital repeatedly looks for ways to acknowledge the importance of its nurses on the healing team and backs this position with promotions and privileges.

The nation's 2.3 million registered nurses often find it untenable when hospitals try to save money by switching nurses' shifts and nurses' assignments, by ordering them to work a second shift, or to care for more patients during night shifts. The shadow that follows them is the fear of making mistakes because of exhaustion.

Cost-cutting demands by managed care and government health plans have been costly to hospitals in their efforts to continue quality care while holding down the price of treatment and specialty staffs in order to qualify for insurance reimbursements.

These problems have provoked nurses in some major cities in the nation to resort to unions, strikes, and walkouts—not just for more money or time off but for more time with their patients. Baptist Hospital has not experienced threats of strikes because its CPS office and administration over the years have been as vigilant about nurses' contentment as it has about new facilities and new technologies.

Thankfully, Baptist Hospital's turnover rate for nurses today remains below the national average of about 20 percent.

A major reason is due to the honor the hospital's Department of Nursing received in late 1999. Baptist is the first hospital in the Carolinas to be awarded "Magnet" status by the American Nurses Credentialing Center (ANCC), the nation's leading nursing credentialing organization. This is the Center's highest award for excellence in organized nursing services in general, acute, special, rehabilitative, chronic, and long-term care. Baptist became the 14th hospital in America to receive this award, which raises it to premier rank. Currently 48 health care organizations in America are Magnet facilities.

The magnet status is valid for a four-year period after which the hospital's Department of Nursing must apply again for status as a Magnet facility. This national recognition program was established in 1993.

Like a magnet, it is expected to attract more professional nurses who want the experience of working in this place of excellence. The award salutes Baptist's management philosophy and practices of nursing services, adherence to standards for improving the quality of patient care, support for continued competence of nursing personnel by the leadership, and attention to the cultural and ethnic diversity of patients, their families, and care providers.

It further acknowledges that Baptist Hospital has created a work environment that recognizes and rewards those providing professional nursing services of quality in an era when triaging patient care is not just confined to emergency medicine.

CPS is as concerned with duty time for nurses and their support staff as it is for the service hours of physicians, physician assistants, residents, interns, and pharmacists.

These certified medical professionals also are acquainted with long hours, fatigue, diminishing respect, cost controls, workload overkill, and authority curtailment by managed care companies.

They, too, want a life with spouses and family, friends, and sleep. They, too, want to recover their patients' faith and trust in their abilities. Increasingly their idealism is being eroded. They fear medicine is turning into a business that hones in on profit, uses "urgent" not to describe a patient's need to be seen by a physician but as a scheduling tool, and demands more time be spent managing rather than treating patients.

Today by new accrediting rules, residents must not work more than 80 hours a week and must have two connecting days off every two weeks. This eases their workload somewhat but not their compassion for their patients' continuum of care. There are limits on how many patients they are responsible for daily, but these rules may be broken when staffing is insufficient or horrific illness demands more team care.

Residents, Pennell explained, have earned their medical degrees, but they are only halfway through their educational experience. They now must spend an additional three to seven years training in their specialties.

Salaries for residents have always been low from their standpoint, but hospital officials and CPS seek to keep them in line with nearby medical schools and teaching hospitals. Acceptance into residency learning programs means accepting the set salaries rather than negotiating pay or work hours.

Baptist residents, in an effort to earn more, over past years have moonlighted at area and community hospitals and diet clinics. This activity is monitored, Pennell stressed, because these physicians-in-training may be asked to perform tasks for which they are not fully qualified. "But at the same time," he explained, "their presence in area hospitals has been a good referral source for us." CPS is not involved in the "outside" work policy, Pennell said. "That is a departmental decision."

Another issue closely akin to staffing shortages is availability of hospital beds.

CPS and the hospital management monitor bed occupancy constantly, for they must balance patient needs with nursing staff. Nurses must be on duty to supply care even when the bed occupancy is low. One major accident on the highways or an epidemic in the community can fill every available bed and make severe demands on the professional services available at the Medical Center, regardless of time of day or patient census.

So bed occupancy is a constant issue on CPS's agenda, for the beds need to be at least 65 to 67 percent occupied if the hospital is to break even financially.

In the past, that percentage rate often could not be met because of fewer service patients and specialties available, discontinued childbirth services, and insufficient air-conditioning.

Later there were shortages of critical care beds, so surgeries had to be scheduled and direct admission to intensive care units (ICU) by outside physicians had to be approved in advance. Triaging of patients was invoked so that beds could be allotted according to the severity of illness or injury.

Often the only way to manage the supply and demand for beds, Pennell said, is to consider early discharge of patients and a more timely and orderly discharge of not-so-sick patients. These days the patient census continues to be high, especially in ICU, often leaving beds reserved for medicine and surgery in very, very short supply, Pennell explained.

When the bed availability is critical, Pennell said, CPS has to consider activating its delay-or-divert policy. This plan was put into effect soon after Pennell became chief. It is one of the few times a decision by the chief stands. There can be no appeals. Without it, the hospital cannot fulfill its mission to provide full-time quality patient care.

The policy was developed, Pennell related, "for those times when the hospital is full and no beds are available, yet patients keep coming for care—often from outside our city—or doctors keep calling, wanting to send patients here.

"So CPS set up a policy as it relates to accepting or delaying patients, specifically critically ill patients. We tell them 'to delay admissions for a few hours and we will try to prepare a place for them.' Or, our answer is, 'We are sorry we cannot take your patient.'" These patients usually are diverted to other tertiary medical centers in the state.

At these times, all admissions are considered on a tertiary basis, meaning patients are accepted at Baptist if they need more care than the hospital where they are or the community hospital where they are to be sent.

"The policy," Pennell said, "is whether to delay a patient's entry or divert the patient. And how can we make room to avoid delay-or-divert. The problem was laid upon CPS not only to develop the policy but also to implement it. It often means that one of the chiefs literally makes rounds on every hospital floor, every intensive care unit, and every critical care unit, et cetera, to identify patients who can be transferred or discharged.

"We open the postanesthesia care unit (PACU) and keep patients there. We keep patients in the emergency room, on operating tables, or any place where they can be safe. All of this planning is under the direction of CPS, working with the directors of ICU and other areas."

There are times when the room crunch is predictable, Pennell said, such as during "RDS (respiratory distress syndrome) and/or RSV (respiratory syncytial virus) times." These breathing-system illnesses that patients, especially young babies, get require special care to improve the risk of complications.

"And it is alleged that some patients are referred to us after 'wallet biopsies,' meaning after seeing how much money patients have, how much insurance they have, how good their insurance is, or how many days their insurance will pay for. The federal government has even written laws to prevent this."

The hardest part of delay-or-divert for Pennell was accommodating requests for beds during no-vacancy times, for if he found one bed, then he would get more and more requests. That's when the chief has to put aside any power pressure and decide on a case-by-case and hour-by-hour basis who could be admitted, who could be released, who could be left on hold, or who could be diverted. That was hard on Pennell, especially when he was dealing with his own colleagues.

But more than that, Pennell confessed, "when we had to resort to the delay-or-divert policy, we were interfering with our commitment to patient care, our referral source, our ego structure, and our income, so it was a hard decision."

Currently the hospital is an 830 licensed-bed facility. Of these, 554 are allocated for general or medical and surgical patients; 144, intensive care; 39, rehabilitation; 49, skilled nursing; and 44, psychiatric. The hospital's total beds include 138 beds in Brenner Children's Hospital and 79 beds in the J. Paul Sticht Center on Aging and Rehabilitation. The Sticht Center can serve 39 inpatients in rehabilitation, 24 in adult psychiatry, and 16 in acute care for the elderly. The Nursing Center at Oak Summit has 170 skilled nursing beds.

Since the Medical Center is designated as a Level One Trauma Center, Pennell said, severe or violent trauma patients are the first admitted under delay-or-divert. Those with less acute problems are sent to other emergency rooms.

CPS leaders make decisions, but their execution often is left to Ala Jo Koonts, the hospital's director of medical staff services and quality consulting. She carries out CPS directives with the assistance of the associate and assistant chiefs. Mrs. Koonts came to work for the hospital in 1975 and thus has worked with every chief except Alexander.

Speaking for the chiefs, Pennell said, jokingly, "There are many who think they run the place, but Ala Jo really does. She has the best antennae for what is going on in this place than any other employee. She has worked her way up through the ranks and unbeknownst to most has earned a master's and a doctorate in hospital administration."

Just as the hospital could not function proficiently without CPS, CPS could not function proficiently without the skilled and patient guidance of Mrs. Koonts, Pennell acknowledged. While the chiefs carry out their full-time commitments as physicians, she carries out the details of the office, calling meetings to clear up problems that can occur within minutes in an organization as large and as diversified as this healing center.

She has the ear of the chiefs who are on call continuously, keeping them aware of potential difficulties. She is credited with having excellent judgment and intuition about when to call the chiefs and how best to solve the worries that could wreck the even flow of hospital care. Past chiefs agree with Pennell that she is an invaluable administrative assistant and organizational genius. She is a necessary continuity if patients are to receive the professional services they expect and demand.

Another continuity is not always as reliable.

It is an issue that causes CPS much worry and constant oversight: the current supply of physicians and those that will take their places in the future.

Health Care Financing Administration (HCFA) is the federal agency that administers Medicare, Medicaid, and Child Health insurance programs and performs quality-focused activities, such as certification of health care facilities, development of coverage policies, and quality of care improvements. Under its quality-care umbrella, HCFA reimburses providers in the fee-for-service Medicare program, allows preventative health care, and supports graduate medical education programs for residents treating Medicare managed care enrollees and Medicaid beneficiaries.

This clinical funding model was changed by HCFA in 1997 when it went to what it called a more cost-effective plan to strengthen and protect Medicare's future. The plan now in progress of implementation continues a course of adjustment. HCFA makes incentive payments to teaching hospitals that reduce the number of their residents and transfers these duties to lesser-trained health care workers. By reducing the number of residents, just one of its proposals, HCFA says it can save billions in Medicare payments.

Another component of the plan, Pennell said, is to get teaching hospitals to concentrate more on training primary care residents and to cut back on an alleged oversupply of physician specialists. HCFA sees these reforms more in line with the needs of the evolving national health care system that increasingly is one of managed care in outpatient treatment centers.

In the past, HCFA claimed that academic teaching medical centers were not true advocates of health care for the poor, for their primary purpose was to educate and train new doctors and research scientists. This view has changed, for HCFA now realizes that academic medical teaching hospitals like WFUBMC provide health care to indigents at a higher figure than that dispensed by community and non-teaching hospitals. HCFA now acknowledges this excellence by reimbursing hospitals for the care of indigents.

Since its inception, CPS has monitored the guardianship of the poor—on campus, off campus, and around the world—and that contribution of evidential compassion increases as the Medical Center grows in size and contributions to medical science.

In 1998, for example, the average statewide bad debt and free care rate of large academic hospitals averaged 5.1 percent while Baptist Hospital averaged 7.0 percent, above Duke University Medical Center with 4.0 percent. Winston-Salem's other major hospital, Forsyth, a not-for-profit facility, had a bad-debt free-care rate of 4.2 percent. Baptist's current free care and bad debt rate still remains at 7.0 percent of total revenues.

Pennell is acquainted with services to the underprivileged, for he has been on the front lines in the battle of their health care all of his professional life. He has served in the trench warfare for the medically indigent locally, nationally, and overseas. Because of his personal involvement, the Medical Center and CPS over the years looked to him for advice when they began expanding safety-net programs for these patients—not because they were poor but because they were sick.

Changes regarding HCFA payments and restrictions have been in progress for nearly two decades, Pennell explained. In the beginning, Medicare paid full cost toward inpatient hospital services and the teaching process of residents.

Then adjustments in payments were made based on teaching hospitals' ratio of interns and residents to patients and also from cost per patient to fixed prices per patient as related to their diagnosis related groups (DRGs) of illnesses.

For patients, it meant quality care by a wealth of physicians and specialists who used wisdom acquired from team-approach medicine to benefit their treatment plans.

Under the most recent formula, called the Balanced Budget Act of 1997 (BBA), which also has been modified, full implementation will be reached in 2002. HCFA said it would cut Medicare and medical reimbursements to hospitals by about $130 billion over five years. This means the Medical Center would experience a cutback of approximately $100 million; however, subsequent readjustments by Congress have reduced those cutbacks somewhat. HCFA says its Medicare medical education payments eventually will be closer to the actual cost of treating Medicare patients at a teaching hospital.

For physicians, it will mean the equivalent of a daily 10k-road race: being clocked for speed, reduced costs, and sociability time with patients.

In the process, creativity and compassion can be stifled along with physicians' ability to practice traditional and alternative medicines.

Pennell defined the issue more succinctly: "If the government does not fairly compensate teaching and training institutions, we will see medical schools closing. We will see hospitals with training programs cutting them back or cutting them out."

So in the process of health care reform and the way it is being managed, academic medical centers are being hurt, Pennell admitted. "Today physicians' incomes have decreased, services they can provide have diminished, and yet cost of care continues to go up.

"The American people may have felt we weren't worth what we were making, but they better decide what kind of health care they want and who they want delivering it in the future, for if we cannot train students to be doctors, then who will?

"The public may think nobody today is doing research like Dr. Alexander Fleming (discoverer of penicillin) did, but this is not true. There are people living right now with AIDS who would have been dead five years ago had there not been individuals out there developing new drugs. The same thing is true for cancer and chemotherapy. The same thing is true for the art of healing—for everything in medicine. Invariably, these kinds of advancements come out of academic medical centers. Physicians do what they do because it is their love, their interest, their covenant."

The American public has the power to change the direction of health care coverage, Pennell believes. "People need to write or contact their Congressmen and let them know how they feel about health care services defined under the Balanced Budget Act. That's what I advise, for the BBA has the potential to destroy us not only from the standpoint of patient care but certainly the possible education of the next generations of physicians."

Now well into its BBA reform payment plan, Medicare is saving money at a higher than expected rate. Teaching hospitals, on the other hand, are adapting to reduced federal medical financial support, increased numbers of uninsured patients, and fewer paying patients. Some are even losing the battle to remain open.

For the past 10 years patient admissions at the Medical Center have decreased, but the severity of illnesses continues to increase. The average daily patient occupancy is 700 people.

Translated, Pennell said, this means that the Medical Center vacancy rate is less than 5 percent, so "we cannot reduce our residency staff and continue to adequately serve our patient population."

The hospital has agreed to retain all filled residency positions at the 1998-1999 level. However, HCFA now will pay only at the capped 1996 level of 414 residents and it will not subsidize any additional residents.

As the Medical Center adds or upgrades a specialty, the need for additional residents is obvious. The hospital then must decide whether it will approve requests for additional residents over the federally set levels. The cost of any new residents will be the hospital's total responsibility. The annual salaries of house staff range from $32,000 to $38,200 yearly. Because of BBA's cut-off rulings regarding residents, the hospital pays about 3 percent more for residents' salaries or about a half million dollars yearly.

Federal officials recognize that in helping themselves toward financial security they have harmed the very ones they proposed to help, thereby cutting lifelines of medical security for millions of Americans. So HCFA is reevaluating its reimbursement relief packages.

For example, HCFA now admits that academic medical centers in the nation like WFUBMC provide high quality research and medical education that is internationally recognized.

It further claims that Medicare has played an integral role in supporting medical education and it must continue this important role—with appropriate input from the American public on the government's role in health care and medical education.

So this is where the public, Pennell reemphasized, can intervene and become involved in true medical care reform.

Physicians may work solo in the beginning of health care recovery as do research scientists, he added, but no one works alone for long, for medical discoveries require teamwork. And one component of that team, he insisted, is the patient—the public—as both recipient and caregiver to the caregivers.

Maintaining a sufficient house staff inventory, therefore, is an ongoing cause of concern for CPS. So is maintaining an ongoing staff of concerned providers.

Maintaining quality health care is not a whim of medicine to CPS, he said. It is a practice that may never be perfect, but it requires that the best providers are needed and available to respond to the worst that strikes patients.

That demands daily 25-hour health care coverage, for diseases neither punch a time card nor ask, "Is this the illness you wanted?"

VI WHEN TO SAY "YES" TO LIFESAVING PROCEDURES

Sometimes CPS must be both judge and jury.

In early 1999, a Medical Center physician asked CPS for permission to use a new procedure for treating malignant cancer tumors. It is less invasive, has fewer side effects, requires a shorter stay in the hospital, and generally speaking may offer faster results.

More importantly, it is often the last treatment hope for some cancer patients.

With credentials like these, who could say "no" to the request?

Sometimes CPS does. It must play the role of judging whether the procedure is safe and if the patient needs it or will benefit from it.

CPS's investigation of the physician's request was intensive and cautious, for who wants to be responsible for not allowing a treatment that might be a patient's last hope. And yet who wants to condemn a patient to eternal pain or despondency should the procedure fail.

The professor of diagnostic radiology had scheduled the procedure, but he followed formalities and sought CPS's approval. After the therapy was explained and the request reviewed, Pennell approved the use of the procedure, called radiofrequency ablation (RFA) of malignant tumors, "in the best interest of the patient's care." However, the physician was cautioned that any further procedures would have to be reviewed in greater depth under prior-approval protocol.

Pennell told CPS that the device used for the procedure "had been approved by the Food and Drug Administration (FDA) for open surgical operations." While new to the Medical Center, he said, nine other medical institutions in the nation at that time were using the technique "on a routine basis."

In radiofrequency abalation, he said, the physician guides a thin viewing tube with a fiber-optic tip into the area of the tumor. Then mild, painless radiofrequency or heated energy—equal to microwave heat—is transmitted to the site. Tumor cells when treated by RFA, he explained, curdle from the applied heat and die, unable to grow or live. In time, the body absorbs these destroyed cells.

Pennell emphasized that RFA is not a replacement for the usual treatment modalities of surgery, chemotherapy, or radiation. Rather, he said, the three treatments can work in harmony as a powerful and effective tool against certain cancers.

RFA's major advantage, he added, is its ability to be used frequently at the same site, particularly where the tumors are hard to access for surgical removal or where the tumors are in multiple abundance, making excision difficult or impossible.

Before granting approval to do the RFA procedure, CPS had to determine if the procedure basically was research or a curative measure.

Some CPS physicians saw it as research and therefore subject to approval by the Medical Center's Institutional Review Board (IRB). Under FDA guidelines, projects involving human subjects must be identified as either for patient treatment or for research, both subject to patient safety and ethical rules. The board-certified diagnostic radiologist defined his new work in RFA therapy as a treatment.

The patient scheduled for RFA suffered from lung and liver metastases following colon carcinoma. The patient's surgeon, in consultation with a fellow surgeon, believed that the most appropriate treatment at that time was radiofrequency ablation since previous anticancer drugs had not controlled the metastases.

The patient was willing to undergo the therapy immediately, aware of possible adverse events following surgery and lack of long-term data on its effectiveness, and was willing to sign an informed consent document, routinely required of *all* surgical patients.

While the procedure is an accepted practice in the ablation of liver tumors, there was less experience at that time with lung metastases. The patient and his family were told the likelihood of the development of pleurisy, the risk of considerable pain, and the possibility of pneumonia due to puncturing the lung in order to deliver the therapy.

The treatment is now being routinely used in 40 Comprehensive Cancer Centers in the United States, including WFUBMC. Most procedures are used on liver lesions, but it also is applied to the vaporizing of cancerous growths at other sites, such as head, neck, breast, bone, prostate, kidney, pancreas, and lung tumors, that fail to respond to the standard treatment of chemotherapy, surgery, and radiation. RFA usually is performed on an outpatient basis. During the procedure, radiofrequency heat is guided laparoscopically into diseased cells for their destruction.

The RFA appliance is analogous to the introduction of other FDA-approved instruments, such as vascular stents, arthrectomy devices, and lasers. These have been used for the treatment of numerous clinical problems. Even though at first some of these procedures were incompletely effective, physicians still deemed their use to be reasonable.

Radiofrequency ablation also is being considered as an alternative therapy for alcohol ablation, chemoembolization, and cryosurgery ablation (freezing tumors to reduce their size), all frontiers not yet fully explored.

Later the radiologist sought permission to do further procedures. This meant more research-and-discovery. The new request was assigned to a CPS committee for study, the usual route of inquiry. It found RFA generally to be purely a clinical application using FDA-approved equipment without any goal to generate new knowledge; therefore, it was not research and thus did not need IRB approval.

However, the study committee encouraged the physician to apply the RFA technique under a research protocol so that in addition to patient care other new knowledge about this procedure could be generated. That would require IRB approval.

Since long-term results were incomplete, the committee felt RFA application should be limited to tumors in patients who were not candidates for more proven therapies.

The group further required that a surgeon with the appropriate expertise from WFUP be involved in the decision to perform RFA and be available to help manage complications, should they occur.

The committee also said that a mechanism for multidisciplinary review and quality assurance of these procedures, involving radiology, surgery, and medical oncology, should be arranged prior to treatment.

By midyear 1999, the physician was granted temporary privileges to perform percutaneous (small punctures through the skin) radiofrequency ablation for a six-month period when privileges would be reviewed. He accepted the guidelines.

At review time, colleagues said he had done an outstanding job developing the RFA program, treated a large number of patients, and achieved gratifying results. He reported that nearly 20 percent of the procedures had not been successful, perhaps due somewhat to the condition of the patient at treatment times.

Fellow physicians urged CPS to continue making this novel approach to cancer therapy available for another six months to highly selected patients with metastatic tumors but still following preprocedural mandated guidelines. The request was approved. Today the procedure continues to be available to patients.

Some RFA patients can be treated under conscious sedation, a procedure that reduces awareness and decreases pain but allows the patient to remain alert enough to respond to verbal commands. In more invasive surgery, patients' consciousness is controlled by a deeper sedation.

Conscious sedation guidelines are defined and monitored by CPS to further the safety of patients.

In the course of its investigation into RFA use, CPS learned that medical institutions already using the treatment did so almost exclusively without IRB approval. It further discovered that the device is currently being employed to treat kidney, pelvic, skeletal, skull, and adrenal tumors.

While surgeons prefer the standard method of cutting out cancerous tumors, Pennell said, approximately 80 percent of the tumors cannot be surgically removed because of their location and metastatic involvement. This new form of treatment is considered both radical and promising in terms of minimizing a patient's risk, ability to continue working, and cost of restoration to health.

Another new instrument for noninvasive surgery in use at the Medical Center is the Leksell Gamma Knife, added in July 1999. This procedure, a form of radiosurgery, uses radiation to treat brain tumors, a process that over time destroys abnormal cells.

The FDA-approved Gamma Knife was the first in the state, then one of only 54 in the nation and one of 135 in the world. It is considered the world's most sophisticated and technologically advanced neurosurgical device for treating brain and functional disorders.

The 18-ton high-tech instrument is used to wipe out tumors, vascular malformations, and other benign and malignant deep-seated intracranial lesions, and to slow or stop some functional disorders such as tremors.

The procedure is an alternative to open-cranial surgery, so it offers new hope for those patients whose lesions often were unsuccessfully treated by conventional craniotomy invasive surgery, chemotherapy, or radiation therapy.

Actually, Pennell said, it is not a knife but a beam using powerful doses of radiation as its surgical scalpel to "operate" on the brain without incision.

Called sterotactic radiosurgery, the procedure works on metastatic malignant tumors and abnormalities located in critical and difficult-to-access areas of the head. The Gamma Knife zaps these lesions with high doses of invisible ionizing radiation and destroys them with such pinpoint accuracy that healthy normal cells are not harmed.

The treatment is faster, has greater energy, causes minimal pain, and is more precise than other radiosurgical tools. It has a better than 90 percent success rate for lesions most commonly treated with radiosurgery, and it also is three times more effective in treating recurrent cancerous brain tumors than other radiosurgical tools.

The knife, which has been in use worldwide for over three decades, brings to medical science proven clinical experience and documentation. Today it is utilized either as the sole treatment or as an adjunct to conventional brain surgery and/or radiotherapy.

The noninvasive procedure minimizes surgical risk and patient discomfort; reduces hospitalization time; and avoids postoperative complications, such as hemorrhaging and infection that can be associated with invasive surgery. Because of short-stay hospitalization, the cost of gamma radiosurgery often can be less than a traditional operation.

The decision to use the Gamma Knife is that of the referring physician and patient in close coordination with a multidisciplinary medical team of specialists, including neurosurgeons, radiation oncologists, neuroradiologists, medical physicists, and neuroimaging and nursing staff coordinators. It is this medical team that develops and implements the treatment plan, tailored individually to each patient's need.

The one-session procedure begins with the patient's unshaved head being placed into a helmet-like frame resembling a futuristic-looking colander. The helmet is secured to the head with four small screws whose tiny wounds heal quickly, leaving no scars.

The rigid frame is necessary to immobilize the patient's head during the next stage of the procedure: high-resolution imaging technology, such as magnetic resonance imaging (MRI), computer tomography (CT) scans, and angiography (X-ray study) to pinpoint the lesion's size and exact site.

This data is fed into a sophisticated computer that maps three-dimensionally the knife's path and dosage. The information is used to position the patient's helmeted head correctly to receive the highly focused radiation shots. The patient is slightly sedated—but awake—during the procedure.

The knife emits a single dose of radioactive cobalt rays, aligned through 201 holes in the helmet, to arrest the growth of the targeted lesion. The gamma rays gain potency only when they intersect at the target site. The treatment causes the tumor cells to stop duplicating and eventually to die.

While alone during radiation, the patient is in constant two-way communication with the medical team that watches the proceedings on video. The patient can be treated and discharged in the same day or may stay overnight in the hospital. The patient may return to previous lifestyle routines within a few days.

Follow-up postoperative visits with the referring physician and radiosurgical team are scheduled to assess the patient's cranial nerve function, hearing, and balance, all rare side effects with Gamma Knife surgery. MRIs of the treatment site are taken annually for four years in order to monitor the progress of the tumor shrinkage or growth cessation. Total obliteration of 80 percent of the treated lesions is expected within two years.

At the Medical Center, the $3 million Gamma Knife is primarily used to treat brain metastases from other tumors such as those arising in the breast, lung, or colon; from primary brain tumors often around nerve cells; and from benign tumors.

The knife's precision allows it also to zero in on pituitary tumors near crucial optic nerves and tangles of arteries and veins that have grown abnormally, often from birth, into and around the brain causing seizures and paralysis.

Persons with trigeminal neuralgia, a malfunction compressing the cranial nerve carrying sensation from the face to the brain, are responding to treatment with the Gamma Knife as it controls severe piercing bouts of facial pain common in the elderly.

And patients with tremors, whether caused by Parkinson's disease, epilepsy, or other disorders, can experience relief from severe shaking and muscle rigidity when administered Gamma Knife radiation.

The Gamma Knife is a major component of the Medical Center's Comprehensive Brain Tumor Program whose radiosurgery division began in 1990.

The Medical Center also continues to offer another treatment outside the range of the Gamma Knife, which is ideal for small-to-medium-sized tumors. Called linear accelerator-based radiosurgery (LINAC-Scalpel), it is an option for larger lesions.

Another noninvasive surgery procedure has been added to the Radiation Oncology Department. The Elekta Stereotactic Body Frame[R] is used for radiosurgical treatment to areas outside the brain, Pennell said. Extracranial body stereotactic radiosurgery (EBSRS) delivers higher and more precise doses of radiation to difficult-to-treat areas, such as the head and neck, spine, lung, mediastinum (the area between the two lungs), esophagus, pancreas, liver, and pelvis—at a minimal risk of affecting healthy tissue.

This combination of treatment options makes the Medical Center one of a few in the world offering the potential of these technological paths for curing lesions of any size and location in the head and body. People with other health issues that make them poor candidates for open surgery are often good candidates for radiosurgery.

Pennell pointed to other new brain cancer procedures now available at the Medical Center. These therapies are part of the many clinical trial programs now in progress in every discipline at the Medical Center.

Trials, he explained, help clinicians find earlier intervention and prevention procedures for the benefit of their patients. Clinical studies are done in controlled phases, he added, under strict scientific guidelines and after approval by CPS and the Institutional Review Board.

In May 2001, a Medical Center team, using the GliaSite[R] Radiation Therapy System (RTS), became the first in the world to treat a glioblastoma multiforme brain tumor or fast-growing and spreading cancer found around the tumor site. Surgery combined with radiation, Pennell said, is traditionally thought to be the single most effective treatment for brain tumors. Tumors are treated with external beam radiation guided into the tumor site. This is a high-risk procedure, for it must pass through and possibly harm healthy tissue. But with the GliaSite system, Pennell explained, the catheter does not release the radiation until it reaches its designated site.

Another exciting experimental brain procedure, Pennell said, involves the medical school as one of 10 in the nation participating in a clinical trial sponsored by the National Cancer Institute. For the first time the school is using gene therapy to treat brain cancers, Pennell said. However, he added, gene therapy has been in use at the Medical Center in various ways for the past decade. In this project, surgeons remove the malignant brain tumor and then insert a genetically engineered virus into the brain cavity to kill cancer cells around the tumor site. The virus is designed to replicate itself as it destroys cancer cells on the cavity margins and halts reoccurrence of cancer at the site.

These examples reveal, Pennell said, that CPS's business is clearly never done in isolation.

"The strength of CPS," he explained, "lies in the fact that the chairs of the various medical school departments sit around that table. That is a significant power base when you stop and think about it—not only from the standpoint of being involved in making the decisions but also for being available for input and for getting these decisions implemented. Without the chairs, we would not get anything done."

While CPS's work more often does involve major life-protecting matters, Pennell added, "high-technology is not all that we talk about. We discuss simple things like physicians and health care providers washing their hands before each patient's examination.

"Or it may be that the chair of the Department of Pediatrics sitting at CPS's table keeps hammering at the importance of people being immunized against rubella (German measles) before they come to work at the Medical Center because of the risk of bringing that infection into the institution. This also is true with regard to everybody getting the flu vaccine. It is important to protect not only the workforce of the Medical

Center but also patients and their families and visitors. When other chairs hear a physician's point, they respect his or her expertise, so they carry the information back to their own departments for implementation.

"This is part of the bubble-up concept so important at the Medicine Center—when individuals remain alert to preventable dilemmas and keep us advised."

When decisions regarding matters such as immunizations come up, Pennell said, CPS appoints special committees composed of professionals working in those related areas to study the matters being considered and then to report their findings.

CPS either approves or reworks the study committee's recommendations. Thus CPS's decisions often are determined from a much wider base of gathered information, for being both judge and jury requires CPS to find the very best of resolutions.

CPS is called upon repeatedly to exercise its judgment as to the credentials of the professional services allowed and provided at the Medical Center and how instruments of care and protection for patients are chosen and implemented.

VII   DOCTORS ALSO MUST BE CHIEFS

The Medical Center's board-certified physicians, in a true sense, are chiefs of the professional services they administer or prescribe within their disciplines.

To be fair to themselves, medicine, and patients, these physicians must remain alert to new and proven advancements, research breakthroughs, and healing techniques that can be applied to their chosen fields of medicine.

They, too, like CPS, must be judge and jury when it comes to patient caretaking.

Physicians listen and then make decisions based on their sworn oath to take appropriate actions: "What is the patient really saying or asking?" "Is the old medicine still working or is there a newer drug that could make life more sustainable?" "Should the patient once again be advised to change the sit-it-out lifestyle of do-nothing?"

In addition to listening to patients, physicians listen to themselves: "Is their compassion audible in the words 'You have cancer'?" "Is their explanation clear on why 'You need an operation'?" "Is there any way to tell patients—kindly—that the symptoms are still evident and are not improving, so 'Are you taking your medication?'"

The key to healing begins with two-way listening and explaining, an art some physicians and patients may never fully achieve, but the clue rests in trying.

That, Pennell explained, is what medicine is all about: trying to ease the disease, the pain, the fear, the inevitable by comprehensive examination, mindful attention, medical detection—and honest interpretation about illnesses and ready responses to patients' questions.

To reach these aims, the leadership of the Medical Center provides an environment of support—an advocacy undercarriage—for its medical shepherds.

The purpose of the Medical Center, Pennell emphasized, "is to provide exemplary and tertiary care—with all that tertiary care encompasses—with compassion, integrity, innovation, and excellence in a flexible and friendly environment based on our heritage, professional expertise, and commitment to education. And part of the innovation is additionally addressed in the third arm of that care, which is research.

"In my own mind, I cannot separate that the Medical Center includes both the medical school and the hospital. Each has different responsibilities, but the overall objectives must be the same. The hospital obviously is more honed in on or alive to patient care and the medical school more on education, but in the Medical Center context, you cannot separate responsibilities or goals.

"The medical school and hospital work together in house staff education and patient care," Pennell stressed. "Research comes down heavier on the medical school side, but we must cooperate even on that. And if we are to stay alive financially, we have to find a means collaboratively to survive the current managed care ultimatums, the Balanced Budget Act, and other, if not opposing, curtailing forces.

"What sets us apart from other medical centers," Pennell continued, "is that we teach medical students. Other aspects of our educational programs are important, too." The medical school has additional studies for house and staff officers; for physician assistants, medical technicians and laboratory scientists, and assistants; graduate degree programs in biomedical sciences as well as medical department specialties; and continuing education for physicians, registered nurses, nurse anesthesiologists, pharmacists, and their associates, and others.

Major within all educational aspects, Pennell said, is the need to teach the medical differentia of compassion—that quality the public seeks along with medicine's curative abilities. "We teach compassion, honesty, and love; and we always have, for there is no other profession where these quality traits are more needed or expected."

To allow medicine to be practiced at its highest known level, Pennell said, leaders and administrators must demonstrate for emulation their trust, shared vision, agreed-upon unified goals, and embedded compassion toward patients who are in awe—and perhaps fear—of the increasing electronic-dispensing of care. Patients yearn for the family-type doctor, that good person willing to care and listen and treat them as a friend.

Patients keep coming to the Medical Center, Pennell pointed out, "because of what we offer. So physicians must keep treating patients according to the basic principle of 'Do no harm' by listening to the patient, establishing correct diagnoses, determining the most appropriate cost-realistic and cost-effective ways of treatment, and by following the Golden Rule. It's about making people well and keeping them well.

"Patients must take an active part in their own care and the prevention of illness. They must be compliant in what they are told to do by their physicians. We all must be aware of smoking, weight, exercise, cleanliness, moral well-being, mental well-being, good diet, enough sleep—that whole series of common things we are responsible for—if we take an active part in the care of ourselves."

Most patients, Pennell explained, enter the circle of care carrying baggage. "It depends upon their own insight. And many, many, *many* other factors: personality, guilt, antagonism, or previous physician encounters that were not good. One of the biggest still is 'I don't want interns treating me.' Another is making sure patients truly understand what we are talking about. And here again, this involves how much insight patients have, how much education, and even how much correct information already has been given to them about their condition."

What many patients may not know, Pennell continued, is that over-looking the care of patients, besides CPS, is the Medical Center's Patient Relations Department.

"When there is a problem with a specific physician or a specific service," Pennell explained, "the Patient Relations Department is there for the patients. That is their challenge, their job description. That is what they are paid to do. It is not to protect us but to be another ombuds-man for patients.

"If a physician does not adequately explain a medical condition to a patient or has a personality conflict with a patient, is consistently two or three hours late for appointments, or doesn't adequately visit with a patient after surgery, then the patient can complain to patient relations. Notice of that grievance is sent to CPS, the chairman of the physician's department, the physician or caregiver, and WFUP's medical director.

"For CPS," Pennell added, "the hardest and most time-consuming problems to handle are patient complaints. It always has been and I think always will be. Closely akin to that is the question of faculty or staff incompetence. Next is the termination of faculty, house staff, and others. CPS presides at all of these appeal processes and that's tough."

What patients care about, Pennell said, is trust, particularly the elderly, for they grew up thinking the physician was a god. Today they have become more aggressive and vocal about their health care, often complaining about the dismissive attitudes of some physicians when they ask questions.

With patients or co-workers, Pennell said, "you don't play games, you don't sweep things under the rug, you don't talk out of both sides of your mouth. When you tell someone you are going to do something to the very best of your ability, then you do it. If somebody confides in you, that person needs to know that confidence will not be broken.

"We need to create a scenario in which people realize that what we are attempting to accomplish for them is in keeping with what is best for them and for the totality of the institution. People honor those they can trust. The role of trust in the life of the physician is profound—as deep as you can get in relationships. Patients trust you as the surgeon to remove all the cancer possible and not tear up the body in the process.

"The same trust level must be there when the physician has to say to the patient, 'You've got myocardial ischemenia (inadequate blood supply to the heart muscle due to coronary artery disease), and you need to have an angiocardiogram (X-ray of the heart and vessels of the heart to detect a blockage or defect of an artery).' Or when you have to say, 'You've got diabetes' or 'You've got AIDS.' You've got to trust your physician."

Pennell has an amazing trust relationship with the medical faculty and patients. They seek his advice, for they value and respect it. In a sense, he is a faculty guru, a powerhouse in times of need and direction. Often they are unaware that he used that trust factor for a round-robin effect to help launch their professional advancements in order that they might reach their full potential.

"I think people share things with me because they trust me not to break confidences, but at the same time they trust me to share that information when appropriate with other individuals. They depend on me to try to bring about change when it needs to be made."

He concedes that he may be trusted simply because of his philosophy of life: "Do for others, as you would have them do for you."

Once a Jewish physician sought him out for help on how to become more involved in overseas benevolent care. "While he knew I was a committed Christian, he also knew I understood his heritage, so he accepted my recommendations.

"Young faculty talk with me about career development, about job offers elsewhere, about how to obtain certain roles and titles as physicians in this institution, about how to resolve personal conflicts in their own departments or between two different departments. I guess they come to me because of my gray hair, for they know I have been around for a long time."

Helping others, he confessed, "is ego-feeding, as it relates to being respected and appreciated. I think it is biblical, one of the tenets of the profession, one of the priority goals and objectives of caregivers. We need to respect everyone with whom we associate, work, or encounter. It makes for a better world, better institution, and better patient care. It makes you do the best you can, and should you fail, you know you gave it your best."

He does it because of another epithet: "Do for others what has been done for you."

"My Christian heritage and commitment and involvement in missions gave me a chance to witness without carrying a Bible or wearing a cross or collar. Simply put: It is the life I have lived. I confess I have blown some of my opportunities, but I hope I made a difference for the people with whom I worked and helped them take pride in this place and in their work. I hope I made a difference in the friendliness and warmth here.

"I had unbelievable rewards in the realm of personal gratification: being able to help people, teach students and residents to strive for higher standards, and correct problems at the patient, professional, and institutional levels. Then there were the people who chose me to treat them—sometimes three generations of a family—and referring physicians who chose me and stuck with me. It's simply this: knowing that I made a difference in patients' lives and that I could make a difference.

"These institutions—both the hospital and the medical school—gave me the opportunity to develop my potential on my terms. They allowed me to be me. They gave me a tremendous amount of freedom—and a tremendous amount of responsibility. They saw the diversity of my personality and interests and allowed me to expand and follow them. What I did and how I did it came about because they allowed me or stimulated me to do it. That is one of the principal reasons I am glad I was here."

Where he made a difference is mostly unseen by the public—and maybe unrecognized by his colleagues. A fellow churchman, now retired from the Medical Center, acknowledged that "the grease gun," meaning Pennell, was quick to address and solve problems and "is sorely missed."

Where he made a difference even further is noticeable in the state of oneness now at the Medical Center, its closest in a long time, thanks to Pennell's mending power.

This harmony also is due to Pennell's political ability to help each side understand each other's mission and agenda. He quietly used diplomacy to help lift up those with leadership qualities so that they were considered for the positions they now hold. To underscore his belief in the institution and those with whom he worked, he nurtured them with loyalty and fidelity. And even when downgraded by invidiousness, he worked silently to restore equanimity and respect—visibly and invisibly.

This unity is growing stronger because of trust between the medical school and the hospital and because "we acknowledge we are a part of a team," Pennell said. "The goal for all of us is exactly the same—or should be—yet at the same time the 'captain of the ship concept' has to be maintained or restored, for somebody has to be in charge. I looked upon myself as serving the ones in charge by being their advisor or counselor, but final decisions were theirs. It goes back to that saying, 'The boss may not always be right, but the boss is always the boss.'"

Over time, he noted, "you got to know your colleagues, what directions they were going, and why they leaned toward their decisions. When there was disagreement, I discussed the pros and cons of an issue with them to make sure each of us involved fully understood the issue and its ramifications. We may have agreed to disagree—and we both may have been right—but the boss is the boss. I don't have any trouble living with that."

Cooperation, whether in the Medical Center or with the Medical Center or other health care providing institutions, is based "purely and simply on trust. That means we must be superior in patient care, education, research, and compassion. We must share that information back and forth, whether between a 20-bed struggling community hospital or tertiary academic medical center elsewhere in the state or nation."

One place where that cooperation has not developed fully, he admits, is between the Medical Center and the local Forsyth Medical Center.

While the two cooperate in some specialty patient care and resident training, there is little evidence of a better relationship with Forsyth, Pennell conceded, "and I don't know how to establish it. I think it can be done only if based on physician relationships—not hospital administration, not medical school administration, or anybody else. It is a tough, tough problem. Should it be undertaken? Efforts have been made over the years, but I think, as long as we are not stabbing each other in the back, that competition is good. I believe patients ought to have the right to choose where they go for medical treatment. If I can't do a better job than someone at Forsyth, that's fine. However, it means we here must continue to offer high quality care and patient-first services.

"Our cadre of patients is fortunate to have this Medical Center with its expertise. We have a distinguished medical staff and faculty. We have an outstanding medical school where the faculty can climb the ladder of recognition nationally and internationally. We have a superbly well-run hospital, which is not going broke like some well-known institutions in the world are.

"We are fortunate to be this academically and financially stable because this medical school and hospital came into being literally on a shoestring, based on our Christian heritage. We are now one of the finest clinical institutions in the nation and our clinical care has been our hallmark. You cannot be an academic institution without good balanced research, and obviously our teaching and research programs, both clinical and basic, have expanded and made a mark for the institution. Because of the demand for clinical excellence, the Medical Center has rapidly climbed to one of the top in the country."

Pennell recognizes that if the Medical Center is to remain renown and maintain its potential, it must coalesce into a single enterprise of health guardianship. That means maintaining a strongly oriented clinical institution that addresses patients' needs first; that claims its tie and commitment to its heritage; that strengthens its patient care, education, training, and research; and that fosters its esprit de corps.

"People love this place and love to work here," Pennell acknowledged, but more and more "people are coming here to work just for the benefits. I don't see as many knocking at our door because they want to be compassionate and caring—except maybe the volunteers.

"Thankfully we have some loyal people at the directorial and managerial levels who set this example. That's where it starts: at the top. And that's the problem. You can't preach compassion. You can't talk it. You've got to demonstrate it. You do that by going down into the bowels of the institution, the guts of the place. That's where you show it.

"When a patient comes in here with AIDS and has a massively bleeding hemorrhoid with a rectal ulcer," Pennell said to illustrate his point, "you expose yourself and every health care worker to the risk of AIDS. You take that patient into the operating room and spend two hours controlling the bleeding. Now am I grateful that I saved this person's life? I can be, but within three to six months his T-cell count will go out the bottom and he is going to come back in here with more infection and die.

"You can be as compassionate, caring, and supportive as you want, but tell me how to be thrilled, heart warmed, and excited by that kind of medical care? While there is no satisfaction there, I must continue to try.

"This is no longer a hip-hip-hooray profession. So would I go into medicine now, knowing what I know? I have asked myself that many times in recent years. I think the answer is 'yes.' It is going to be a totally different medical ballgame in this century. Everybody says that I came through the door of the medical profession during the Golden Age and I believe I did. The new generation of physicians and health care providers will be able to do many things with new technologies that I can't even imagine, but they still must have an inclination and inherent ability in technology as well as personal concerns and skills. The fact that compassion still is a craft will be true and still will be needed.

"If the Medical Center ever loses its compassion—its personal touch and personal care of patients—its future will be threatened. If we aren't better and if we don't demonstrate improved results for sicker patients, then we are not doing what we should. I don't think there ever has been a question about the quality of care here, but we do have to work at being more caring because we have gotten so big. We must continue to be chiefs over the professional services we administer and we must couch that care in the language of compassion. That spirit permeates this place and makes it unique."

That compassion is defined by many as a discernible, yet invisible, quality that is as mysterious as healing. Seasoned physicians encounter it, as do novices. Insiders acknowledge it. Outsiders call it remarkable. It is healing at the spiritual level.

The Medical Center owes its life to this spirit. It was born as a missionary effort by North Carolina Baptists who poured their Sunday money into weekday expenditures for the care of the sick and the poor. Baptist Hospital opened with hardly a widow's mite for existence. Early on its financial condition—based on a depression and wrought by a world war—was often only a step removed from Code Blue, a medical signal for disaster.

Still it survived and grew. Less than two decades from its founding, the hospital entered partnership with Wake Forest College and its school of medicine. Early on, the Medical Center was the patient: unhealthy, depressed, and undernourished financially. Its money flow remained borrowed and blue.

The medical complex however no longer is vexed by bankruptcy. Many of its internal problems have healed. It has grown from a community hospital to a major one known internationally for its vanguard technology, research, and clinical practice. It still aches to practice its skills rather than yield to commercialism or selling its product.

While its birth spirit still permeates, its force has dimmed. But the sacred mission of health care still exists amidst this moral and scientific enterprise. No one person can claim credit for its existence, but many want the claim credited. Those who helped to found the Medical Center possessed this spirit. Those they taught or influenced inherited it. Those coming in now either accept it, make peace with it, or move on.

As one longtime staffer put it: "This place almost adopts you, and you become dedicated to making it continue to grow. It allows you to reach your potential. We have our failures, simply because of the kinds of problems that people bring to us. On the other hand, the successes sometimes are incredible. So our people can get their positive strokes from knowing that they have done their very best. And very often that is enough."

VIII FUTURE OPTIONS AND CONSUMER DEMANDS

From birth the body begins to age and over time it becomes less efficient. People become patients when their impatience with the body's breakdown propels them to medical caregivers for intervention.

In the race for a good life, people no longer are content with either "take-two-aspirins-and-call-me-in-the-morning" medical advice or mortgaging the house to pay for it. They want what they want, and what they want is quality medical services now and at a reasonable rate.

This also is what the medical profession wants to provide for patients.

In that offering, the scope of care is ever enlarging at the Medical Center.

"We are criticized sometimes for being too big, but one of our strengths," Pennell emphasized, "is our 'one-stop shopping,' if you will. You can come in and get everything done at the same complex without having to move from site to site. Our first commitment is to patient care and then to the education of medical students. If what we do is not patient-oriented, then I really question our financial support of it.

"I think the public appreciates us because we are an academic medical center—a factor in our behalf—and because of our reputation for outstanding health care. There are those who realize that by coming here their lives or the lives of family or loved ones have been saved or extended and they appreciate that."

While science is currently able to repair, replace, and rejuvenate many of the body's weaknesses, more than ever before, Pennell acknowledged, science cannot always sustain life longer than the life span determined by the genes and cells inherited—but the possibilities are increasing.

This means, he added, that the medical profession today must consider future options and consumer demands and how to serve both while balancing quality, expenditures, and services in light of restrictions by health insurance plans.

This will call for hard decisions—nothing new to medicine, Pennell said. Many will be based on moral and ethical principles which society often refuses to act on legally—nothing new to medicine, he acknowledged. These decisions often deal with questions on when death occurs and who should have access to patients' medical files and genetic codes? Then there are the issues of euthanasia, gene therapy, organ transplantation, and experimentation on humans.

The earthquakes waiting to rock the medical Richter scale, however, are the mounting epidemic-like medical problems spreading across all socioeconomic lines: the tremors of drugs and AIDS and other breakdowns in the body that result from substance abuse and the plagues of debilitating illnesses on the body's organ systems.

And then there always is—in medicine's arena—the shakiness of insurance coverage. It determines what can be done and whether patients can hope for a future.

If not checked, the vastness of these problems could break the nation's financial medical underpinnings, carrying along with it medicine's response capabilities and people's ability to receive the health care they desire.

The devastation could flow down the medical chain, its vibrations reaching even this Medical Center, Pennell warned. The tertiary system of care could be shattered if infections from unsafe sexual practices, use of recreational drugs, and "so-be-it" attitudes about health care in general are not curbed.

The Medical Center cannot dictate mores or other pervading attitudes, he said; however, it must provide treatment for their byproduct illnesses along with prevention education.

AIDS, which had shown signs of stabilizing at the start of year 2000 because of aggressive drug intervention, is now showing a tendency to increase as are gonorrhea and syphilis. The realization is clear: The AIDS epidemic is not over in America or the world.

The attitude of "nothing left to lose" may prevail among those with infections, for once again many are now reverting to pleasure practices rather than safety measures. At the moment, available AIDS medical dollars are being used more for prevention than cure. The most effective cure, public health officials believe, lies within a surefire vaccine, but its discovery seems at least a decade away. Many pharmaceutical firms are competing in this research in the hope to be the finders and keepers.

Meanwhile, the medical profession urges Americans to follow precautionary intimacy practices to prevent HIV/AIDS, hepatitis B, genital warts, chronic genital herpes, gonorrhea, and syphilis.

"Few disease processes, including plagues, tuberculosis, or cholera epidemics, have had the diversity of emotional response that AIDS has provoked in the citizenry of this country," Pennell said, "and it involves all segments of society. AIDS' cost to this country, the world, and society is truly astounding.

"A greater impact is going to come from drug use and drug users. If you compare us to Miami, New York, Chicago, or San Francisco, I think the number of drug-related injuries we see every week is truly staggering. People breaking into houses and getting shot or stabbed or having automobile accidents are often directly related to drug use."

Addictions usually occur, he explained, because individuals take drugs to induce feelings of pleasure, to relieve stress, and to block pain. Drug abuse, he added, knows no boundaries in the socioeconomic makeup of America.

"We are seeing more addiction problems today than 20 years ago. The incidences are higher and it is less of a closet disease, so when a patient with an addiction asks for help, I see this as a major first step. Motivation is an unbelievable component."

Of the addictions—depressants (downers), stimulants (uppers), and hallucinogens—Pennell said, "some are obviously socially acceptable. Alcohol and tobacco have been the tradition. Tobacco is now being addressed by public pressure. Alcohol has not felt that sting yet, but it will and should.

"Neither is probably as acutely devastating as synthetic narcotics. Crack (cocaine) is bad and a rapidly destroying preparation. My contention all along has been that pot (marijuana) may or may not be as bad. However, the use of pot can associate individuals unequivocally with an element in society that wants to get them on something else. It leads to the use of other drugs when the affects of pot are not sufficient and when one is still looking for that high or response. That is one of the major problems with pot, as far as I am concerned.

"There is a great variance in the ages of drug users. There are not many old people who live with addictions—aside from alcohol and tobacco. There are 90-year-old people who have a drink, or maybe two or three, every day, or who smoke three or four cigarettes a day, or chew or dip. But those who are in their late teens, twenties, and thirties are the ones most in trouble, for they are wiped out in their forties and fifties or they are institutionalized or something like that."

The use of marijuana as a way of alleviating the pain and nausea associated with cancer, AIDS, terminal illnesses, and other diseases is under new scrutiny, Pennell said, not as a pretense of legalizing it but to determine if it has medical value.

"I am not sure if the present war on drugs, as currently put together, is the answer. Education is an extremely important part of it. Motivation is, too. I am not sure what the answers are. There are those who believe—because of the current percentage of our population on drugs—that this country must seriously reconsider legalization of drugs. They believe that this will take the criminal element and dirty-needle scenario out of the disease and would decrease the incidents of AIDS as related to drug usage.

"All of this tremendously impacts on health care resources and facilities," Pennell said. "I do not think anything has ever impacted medicine the way AIDS has or will."

Pennell believes a cure for AIDS will be one of medicine's next major discoveries and will be a measure of what medicine can do for the public, for it not only will save lives, but it also will decrease inpatient care and devastating drug cost.

Pennell began studying drugs and their misuse in the mid-1960s when, as a resident and instructor in surgery, he began encountering drug-related trauma patients. Basically the only drug information being offered then was by the Winston-Salem Police Department, but young people did not trust the police even though they were doing a good job, Pennell recalled. He realized that people were not accepting the community's drug problems, so he took his concerns to schools, colleges, and civic clubs. "I must have made 500 talks on drug abuse, its effects, its problems." He helped in getting drug education, treatment, and rehabilitation programs started. "I had to learn a lot about the various drugs being abused. I had to learn about addiction, unwanted side effects, and impurities. It frightened me to think of its effect on society as a whole as well as what it could do to individual families. I knew if we could not find some solutions to mood alteration, then as a society we were in serious trouble.

"People use drugs as an escape mechanism, an escape from problems that I hope a growing number now realize are best dealt with in other terms, whether the problem is rebellion within a family, hunger, poverty, rejection, or hopelessness.

"It was a soul-searching period, but I learned a lot, especially from young people. Because of my age, profession, and Christian commitment, I was perceived as belonging to the Establishment. And that taught me how to better listen to those who were not."

When drug problems infiltrated the Medical Center, he and others had the knowledge to help, especially with policies and guidelines. Drug use, he emphasized, "is something that simply cannot be tolerated" in the Medical Center's environment.

As for the Medical Center, it established its Center for the Neurobiological Investigation of Drug Abuse to provide increased knowedge to the medical school faculty and students, as well as the public, into the biological mechanics underlying compulsive drug use behavior and the development of compounds for clinical treatment. The National Institute on Drug Abuse (NIDA) funds this research training center.

One of the major research efforts of this center, Pennell said, is examining the relationship between compulsive drug abuse and the brain's processes. Researchers concluded that the age a child begins to smoke cigarettes has a high correlation to other health-risk behaviors. For example, middle school-aged adolescents who begin smoking cigarettes at age 11 or younger engage in twice the number of potentially life-ending behaviors. These include riding in a car with a drinking driver, carrying a knife or gun to school, fighting, having a suicide plan, or using marijuana, cocaine, the synthetic drug Ecstasy, or inhalants. Inhalant use is increasing primarily because of its easy availability and powerful effects. Drug use intensifies when users seek higher and longer thrills. What they often get are permanent bodily disorders and entry into a destructive life.

With the new century, the Medical Center is accelerating its participation in understanding human genes—the creation acid that defines a person's genetic makeup. This interest dates to 1941 when the medical school pioneered the first medical genetics department in the nation, attached to its Department of Pediatrics.

Gene reading may be the greatest stride in medical understanding in the 21st century, Pennell said. Once gene knowledge is harvested—and harnessed—he believes it will create a new era in medicine, underscoring how medicine will approach each person's care.

Gene research may make it possible to treat diseases long before their symptoms are detected, he said. And drugs may be formulated to deter human disorders by treating them with medications and dosages that can be tolerated.

Full understanding of the gene book of life is not likely to be known immediately, Pennell realizes, but genes' capabilities increasingly will become better known as scientists learn each gene's distinctive properties and assignments.

To enlarge its over 60-year probe into gene understanding, Pennell said, the medical school established a Center for Human Genomics at the Medical Center in 2000. Its research and clinical scientists and molecular biologists have been participating in the federal government's Human Genome Project at the Department of Energy and National Institutes of Health begun in 1990.

The human genome biography is expected to be completed by April 2003, and in another 20 years each gene's role in disease is expected to be identified, Pennell said. By then genes' family trees, characteristics, and behavior will be computer captured, making known genes' role in promoting or correcting health.

Hundreds of scientists from around the world, including researchers at this Medical Center, are part of a consortium of academic medical centers involved in human genome research. They are disentangling the genetic structure of humans as found in their DNA (deoxyribonucleic acid), a double spiral ladder-like structure that holds clues to the role of genes on possible health abnormalities. These researchers are sequencing the three billion chemical units or letters within the DNA, inherited from each parent, in the hope of identifying genes linked to diseases in order to develop treatments to improve them.

The genome's code basically is a four-letter alphabetical jumble of A's, C's, G's, and T's—somewhat like a game of Scrabble™ waiting to be clarified. Scientists are using computer programs to convert these letter sequences into database equations that could eventually unravel the mysteries of gene structures. From there they can leapfrog to intervention discoveries as physicians design drugs, therapies, and treatment programs based on patients' genetic analyses, Pennell explained.

Computers are the next-stage technological instrument on which research is being done. They are translating the gene's alphabet into understandable formulas and storing the information on gene structure, location, size and shape, and bodily use. With this database, researchers can combine the information with virtual reality and look at patients' abnormalities in 3-D, thus better enabling scientists and physicians to plot approaches to medical correction.

Some Medical Center researchers, for example, are currently focusing on genomics-based therapeutics, especially the discovery and development of drugs to treat cancer and other diseases. Their research participation is in connection with the Medical Center's Comprehensive Cancer Center and a leading biopharmaceutical company.

Another project involves generating an embryonic monkey stem cell line from which brain neurons and heart muscles, to name two, have been produced through a process called "parthenogenic cloning." This research has the potential of finding ways to treat specific diseases like Parkinson's and Huntington's through clinical transplantation of corrective cells.

Gene therapy already is in use at the Medical Center, Pennell said, as physicians participate in clinical trials like one using a live virus engineered to destroy only diseased cells in reoccurring malignant brain tumors. The drug also has the potential to replicate itself at the cancer site as needed.

Knowledge gained from the current rough draft identifying the human structure will recast the way medicine will be practiced and understood in the future, Pennell believes, but the deciphering will not be an overnight accomplishment because of decoding complexity.

Curing the body's vulnerable troubles is more than gene understanding, Pennell explained, for scientists are finding that factors like human spirit, faith, environment, nutrition, and exercise also influence the body's development and regeneration. And, he added, researchers also now believe that the body can be taught to heal itself.

Once science is able to determine patients' genetic compositions, then it can determine which of their genes are abnormal or causing cells to function abnormally. This eugenic information, Pennell said, could be used in counseling couples in family planning, to correct genetic defects, and to investigate early-warning signals before catastrophic illnesses cripple—whether in natural pregnancies or *in vitro* fertilization—but, he stressed, embryonic testing is *not* for abortion decisions.

"I think the detection of inherited problems that babies acquire *in utero* or before birth, such as extra fingers, will improve along with *in utero* correction—when it can be done. This also will be true for congenital heart problems.

"Once we get a better handle on genetics—and we will—many of the congenital anomalies will be identified *in uteri*. I think in the near future, when couples begin to get serious about having children, we can get a genetic picture that will predict what their offsprings will be like."

By knowing the probable genetic composition of the lives about to be created, Pennell explained, "we will be able to recognize which babies will be confronted with diseases before they are formed so that measures to prevent, control, or decrease the diseases' magnitude can be taken."

A large segment of families who now come to the Medical Center for genetic counseling, Pennell said, "has a high propensity or incidence of familial polyposis of the colon due to their own genetic makeup, and, therefore, a large segment is predisposed to developing cancer. So their colon may need to be removed. We now can detect which members of the family will get it and which members are predisposed to the development of carcinoma.

"The time may well come," he continued, "when people will order their babies. To some degree that exists in some segments of society today, for with all of the prenatal studies being done, the detection of abnormalities and sex can be determined. If you think the cloning of sheep caused an uproar, what about cloning humans?"

With genetic developments, Pennell added, one of the key issues will be "how medicine, religion, and society will deal with changing the genes or genetic makeup." Once genetic markers and genes are identified, people could be structured to live long past 100, Pennell predicts.

These ethical decisions "will involve not just medicine, for they will be made jointly with society," Pennell said. "There are those who allege that the medical profession does not police itself on ethical issues, and this simply is not true. I don't think any other professional group polices itself as closely—just look at the role of CPS. It is interesting that society has varying viewpoints ethically while medicine comes out almost uniformly ethically. I am always impressed with the impact of the Judeo-Christian heritage and concept on medical ethics. I think that is appropriate and one of the trends I hope we will never lose."

Pennell believes that the federal government will prevent any misuse of the genetic code's manual of answers. The primary purpose of the project, he believes, is solely to improve and enhance health care effectiveness—but under the precaution of patients' privacy so that genetic data cannot be used indiscriminately by insurance and medical providers or employers.

From patients' perspective, knowing ahead of time what health difficulties they are prone to inherit or what drugs they cannot tolerate may give them an opportunity to enter seasons of prevention or correction. Americans have come to expect physicians to have a curative medical bag from which to work magic on *all* disabilities, and they often do not see themselves as prevention subscribers.

The medical school's new genetic center is focusing on areas where research already is strong in common and often complex illnesses, such as cardiovascular and kidney diseases, cancer, neurosciences, diabetes, asthma, children's disorders, rehabilitation, and aging. A genetic research team recruited from the University of Maryland has joined the genetic center in its discovery walk toward further gene therapy application. One of the next national genome projects will be understanding the complex set of proteins, the body's acids necessary for growth, development, and health.

The new genetics center supports the Medical Center's ongoing research into developing treatment drugs, developing gene therapies through animal research, and putting drug discoveries into use in clinical practice and disease prevention.

Stem cell research, Pennell emphasized, will be conducted under the usual ethical and moral standards followed at the Medical Center and under CPS's regulatory supervision.

These and other miracles-in-the-making continue to mature on Hawthorne Hill.

IX   WONDERS OF MEDICINE, WONDERS OF THE BODY

As scientists scramble to uncover more and more of the body's cryptic formulas, they also persevere with problems they daily address by deepening their understanding and appreciation of the body's wonders and how to address impairments.

It may be the "Age of Genomics" in science, Pennell admitted, but it always is the season for critical reexamination in medicine—a constant in the role of CPS and those who interpret its decrees.

It is one thing to wonder but another to work wonders.

Pennell has seen both as chief and surgeon.

"I think the human body is the most magnificent of all creation. There is no doubt in my mind that God created it and how we got to where we are. I am not what is considered a creationist, as opposed to an evolutionist, but there is no doubt that God created, through whatever means, a body as involved as this most magnificent piece of machinery.

"How complex and how organized and how functional the human body is remains one of the overwhelming insights I have gained from my profession. I never cease to be amazed at the totality of it. The more we learn about it, the more amazed I become.

"Then there is the propensity of the body to heal itself when something is destroyed or harmed through infection or injury. If one allows the healing process to take place without interference, it will heal.

"Also remarkable is the propensity of patients to recover from staggering physical, emotional, psychological, and other horrendous events.

"This whole concept of DNA and genome typing is a marvel as is the whole concept of anatomy and the interplay of muscles, nerves, tendons, the blood supply—all of that. Stop and think about a 300-pound professional athlete being able to pick up a straight pin between his thumb and any other of his fingers. Think about the ability of the anal sphincter being able to differentiate between the states of matter and the need to pass gas or maybe a stool and the interplay between the muscles for relaxing or for holding. We go all day long and don't even have to think about continence and the work of the sphincter. Then when we need to stool, suddenly that automatic mechanism relaxes and switches to an internal mechanism that tells us our rectum is full and we need to eliminate it. It's remarkable.

"Then there is the whole concept of the human eye and vision. I don't see how anybody, when they stop to think about it and learn more about it, cannot stand in absolute awe of the human body.

"So it is with deep respect that I treat others' bodies—even though I don't always treat mine—with equal respect. 'What is the hardest part of the body to treat?' isn't the question, but rather, 'What is the hardest disease process to treat?' There almost is no place in the body that we cannot now go or gain access to—somehow or other.

"There are those disease processes we better understand now, such as cancer. While there is a resurgence of tuberculosis, it is not what it was when I came through medical school. Smallpox is now—and we pray it remains—almost a disease of the past," Pennell said, referring to threats by terrorists to use smallpox and anthrax as biological weapons.

Of the two, he said, smallpox is more feared because it is a highly communicable virus that has a high morbidity and mortality rate. Although smallpox hasn't occurred in America since 1949, he added, its return could be devastating to health care protectors, for the nation is not yet fully prepared for widespread cases of smallpox.

Many consider a smallpox outbreak unlikely, he said, but the government is fending off possible attacks by ordering new vaccine supplies and by diluting existing reserve vaccines to protect, as needed, patients as well as medical, law enforcement, and public health caretakers. The federal response plan, he said, includes quarantining the victims and vaccinating those who came in close contact with the infected.

"We must recognize," Pennell reminded, "that routine inoculations against smallpox were discontinued in this country in 1972 and the disease eradicated in 1980, which means a major segment of Americans—many in the health care profession—have little or no immunity. Plus, we must train medical providers to recognize smallpox symptoms."

Health care professionals also must address other deliberate bioterrorism acts such as anthrax attacks, Pennell said, for anthrax spores are easy to produce and dispense and they can be deadly but not contagious. Patients usually respond to antibacterial drugs.

As in the case of any threats to health care, Pennell explained, CPS must implement its operational plans for patient and caretaker safety.

"We have made progress in a lot of areas, but we must be prepared in new areas as they affect the well-being of our patients. A lot of disease processes unfortunately have changed because some have been mismanaged. Staphylococcal infection is one of them. We probably could have avoided some earlier diseases, currently methicillin-resistant, by using antibiotics more appropriately in the past."

Researchers have discovered the genetic code of staph, so they now hope to develop a vaccine to fight this leading cause of infections acquired in hospitals and increasingly immune to drugs, Pennell explained. People prone to staphylococcal infections include newborns, those with chronic diseases or skin conditions, and those recuperating from surgical incisions. All people have staphylococci in their nose and on their skin, and most of the time this staph does no harm, but a tear in the skin can allow bacteria to enter the body and cause abscesses, such as boils and infections in the heart and its valves. Antibiotics are used as treatment.

CPS, Pennell noted, always keeps an eye open to formulary expense as related to antibiotics—more than any other drug group—and what they are being prescribed to do, reviews the hospital infection rate, and requires precautionary policies on resistant microorganisms.

It is able to take this overall view because CPS-appointed pharmacy and infection control committees constantly monitor these areas. These committees report any formulary problems to CPS, which the chiefs then act on.

"One thing I see coming in the future," Pennell fears, "is a significant increase in the number of resistant bacteria microorganisms," which can be found everywhere in the body, particularly in the airways, mouth, intestines, and on the skin. Usually they can live in harmony within a healthy person, but they can become harmful. The diseases they can cause depend on the body's natural defenses, he explained.

"We already are seeing methicillin-resistant staphylococcus, which is resistant to most antibiotics. I think we are going to see this infection increase, and I think the very lax use of antibiotics to treat everything will cause us to go through another educational phase to redesign and redevelop drugs" that will be effective against infections.

New antibiotics are developed frequently, Pennell realizes, but some of the "new ones are not as effective against resistant bacteria. You've got 15 to 20 drugs you can use to treat a strep throat but virtually few new drugs to treat the resistant staphylococcus.

"There is an unbelievable and widespread feeling among patients that if the doctor 'would just give me an antibiotic, I could get through this cold'—or whatever the complaint. But when an antibiotic doesn't work, patients say, 'Well, you gave me the wrong antibiotic, so give me another one.' Or, 'Why didn't you give me x-y-z?'"

Patients want to use antibiotics inappropriately, he added, and in so doing, there is the danger that the bacteria will develop resistance to these wonder drugs so needed for treating more serious infections. Some of the new antibiotics are not as effective against the new strain of tuberculosis because it is resistant to drugs. No one wants to see this disease become uncontrollable again, Pennell said, and the same is true with the new drug-resistant strains of gonorrhea and syphilis.

"We also may be back to an increasing era of osteomyelitis (a bone infection caused by bacteria or fungus) and mastoiditis (an infection of the bone behind the ear) because parents are becoming more lax in getting their children to take medications" for the fully prescribed period.

So the need for new and effective antibiotics, Pennell said, is critical in order to combat the infectious diseases that are not checked by most antibiotics, those diseases that invariably spread through hospitals, health care facilities, and across a community.

"The best way to learn about new medications," Pennell said, "is from medical journals or by participating in drug trials in which you and your colleagues in your institution—and certainly in this institution—actually test the drugs and their results for protocol studies."

The principles on infection prevention, Pennell explained, are taught early in medical school. "There are laws under which wounds heal. I tell my students that only God can heal a wound. I cannot. I can do things that enhance the healing of that wound. If you avoid contamination and tissue injury, then you call upon the phagocyte cell to do its principle work and eat bacteria cells. If you injure the tissue by squeezing it too hard during surgery or by leaving dead tissue behind, then the phagocyte cell 'cleans up' the problem and cannot focus on just vacuuming the bacteria that causes infection, so there is poor or no healing.

"This is one of Koch's[7] basic principles," he said. In his postulates, "Koch spelled out the things you must be able to do scientifically to prove something. His basic concept was this: If a question is raised and you provide the answer and you can duplicate experimental evidence with the same results every time you continue to get positive reactions and positive results, that confirms the postulate."

For example, to treat cancer of the colon, "you take the cancer out, you take out a length of damaged bowel or intestines, and then you sew the bowel together. If in the postoperative period, the patient does well immediately and also over the long haul, you add this treatment plan to other colon cancer surgeries.

.

[7] German surgeon and bacteriologist Robert Koch (1843-1910) devised a test to prove that a specific microbe causes diseases or lesions. This test became known as "Koch's postulates," standards that are still followed in medicine. He opened the way for unbelievable advances in the conquest of bacteria-causing diseases.

"That basic principle has not changed in 100-plus years. One that has is the way we prep the wound or prep the skin prior to making the wound. When I first started in surgery, we did a 10-minute scrub, almost by the clock. It is now down to a three- to five-minute scrub. That's changed, but the basic principle is still there. What hasn't changed is the principle of washing your hands before examining each patient.

"Another basic principle is doing a detailed medical history and physical examination. You want to develop a diagnostic tree with differential diagnoses. You want to decide what is the most probable diagnosis. Then you want computers to come into play, which they can, and this greatly enhances, in some situations, the things we process—ruling in or ruling out. This all leads to evidence-based diagnosis and a treatment tree that everyone should adhere to in order to decrease cost and hone in on problems.

"A physician who suspects the patient of having ulcerative colitis can push a button and the computer tells him or her that this is the most expeditious way to arrive at that diagnosis, this is the recommended plan of treatment, this is the outcome that can be expected. But it still goes back to the basic principle of doing a basic history and physical examination and then assembling the information and arriving at a diagnosis. I think it is imperative that the concept of the detailed history and physical exam be maintained—and in some instances restored. And I think it is essential that you keep educating yourself and learning the new technologies in medicine.

"What you learn in medical school is basic information to build on during a residency. The reason for all the changes that have taken place in the various curriculums has been to instill and teach the concept of constant ongoing education. When you go through a residency, there are basic principles that you learn that will never ever change.

"On these basic concepts then, the individuals who keep up and do what they should be doing are undergoing a constant and continuing medical educational process. That's the reason Continuing Medical Education (CME) requirements came into being. In that component, I think the greatest majority of physicians have taken care of themselves and it has worked well. That is the reason we go to national meetings: to keep up with the latest advents in techniques and results. That is the reason we read medical journals. That is the reason we read textbooks when the information is finally put into print.

"Those of us in academic medical schools develop and expand new techniques. It is part of our job and our responsibility. It is not only to improve patients here but to educate our colleagues in our specialties.

"There is an old adage that we hammer into our students and our residents: 'Be not the first by whom the new is tried or the last to lay the old aside.' That's applicable to the good strong clinician in private practice. There are times when we in our environment have to be the first by whom the new is tried to determine if it works."

He pointed to the introduction of laparoscopic cholecystectomy in 1990 as an example. "There were skeptics," but this technique for gallbladder removal has proved to be a revolutionary surgical practice. "It has stood the test of time, now being used for 95 percent of all gallbladder removals. This has led some physicians to try to do everything with laparoscopy, from taking out the colon and diseased spleens, fixing hernias, and even for coronary heart bypasses and brain surgery. Patients should be sure their surgeon is trained and experienced in the surgery they are to undergo."

A laparoscope or fiber-optic instrument consists of a lighted tube with magnifying lenses used to enter the body through a small incision, usually in the abdominal wall, for visual inspection and treatment, he explained. Since it is major surgery, he added, it should be performed by trained and experienced physicians.

"By the time the laparoscopic cholecystectomy came forward, I had reached the age in my life when I decided that I was not going to do it. I had learned the techniques and could do it and knew I could, but I decided we needed to leave this technique in the hands of younger people. So without bias, I decided I was not going into laparoscopic surgery. Other physicians made the same decision.

"The technique has developed and developed well and is now a commonplace procedure. Residents have been well trained and are well skilled at it, and they will carry this as a basic principle—video-gaming or doing surgery on a television screen—in their practice just like the basic principles that I brought out of my residency.

"I was fortunate to have faculty who made clear the basic principles that were important. It's part of what you learn through the long period of medical school and residency training. Each branch of medicine has its own unique basic principles. And they are reinforced every day."

As a medical educator, Pennell used the new technologies, but he insisted that his computer-dependent students use their "human computer"—the brain—as their encyclopedia of medical-captured knowledge. When teaching, he asked his students to shut off their computers on which they were taking class notes and listen.

Listening is a trait he hopes future physicians continue to learn, as they deepen their professional walk into medicine as caretakers, for listening is a basic principle from which to capture the clues needed to cure the magnificent body when it encounters a season of fever.

X SEEING THE BODY AS PHYSICIANS' WORKPLACE

One of the few constants in the lives of physicians is change, an unshakable shadow. Often physicians feel *they* have become the shadow, trying to keep up.

It is not just new patients with new ailments that make physicians run. It is new societal pressures, new concepts to medical treatment and patient care, new ethical decisions, new encroachments from public purse-holders. CPS shadows these demands.

Unchanged are the desires of physicians: to return patients, as nearly as possible, to wholeness and wellness.

CPS is the overseer in this process and is quick to react when there are deviations from its disciplined mission to protect the flagstaff phrase: *"Take me to Baptist."*

With CPS as its protector, this designation of excellence remains a basic principle. And the Medical Center remains an honored place that breeds physicians dedicated to the principles of curing body and soul, mind and matter. Textbook knowledge joins reality and possibility at the hospital bedside. The hospital is deservedly known for its excellence in specialized, advanced, and centralized services by knowledgeable personnel; its revolutionary disease management; and its high-tech wizardry treatment possibilities—as well as individual initiatives from its health care professionals.

People today want their medical experience—whether in sickness or health—to be at the hands of those who are the best of clinicians: physicians with the family-doctor disposition, nurses and therapists with cool hands and warm hearts, researchers with an unquenchable thirst for answers.

Patient care of tomorrow is often available today at the Medical Center because research can be quickly mainstreamed to patients, so patients go there for that quality of comprehensive care.

CPS acquiesces in all of these desires.

Pennell, speaking from his service experience as chief, recognizes that what was once a small, regional hospital has grown into one of the nation's preeminent academic medical centers, and now medical and scientific personnel, students, and patients seek entrance because of that excellence. People come to the Medical Center, he added, for its earned reputation of doing things right and doing them well.

Physicians seek to join the staff because of this prestige, but more often the Medical Center selects those it wants. This process of recruitment, Pennell said, "is very selective" and physicians are sought "for special needs in research, teaching, and clinical care. We try to identify the best possible candidates—from the nation or world—who will meet our needs. This will continue into the future as we keep realigning, restructuring, and enlarging. Our goal is to keep focused on the needs of our patient load."

Listening to and learning from every patient and every consultation with other physicians, Pennell said, is combined with acquired medical knowledge. "If you don't learn from every patient you encounter—even from routine mundane hernia, hemorrhoid, or biopsy—you are shortchanging yourself and those with whom you work and those you treat. One of the strengths of this place is the willingness to pitch in and help—whether it is a formal or informal consultation. There is a wealth of experience and knowledge here.

"Medicine as I have grown up in it and know it—and I span a lot of years now—is radically different, as seen in the total field of computerization, both diagnostically, therapeutically, and in every other way. I learned that if I keep my 'computer'—my recall—going appropriately, it makes a difference in what can be done for patients."

Pennell has two basic questions when it comes to patients: "What does this person really need?" "How can I best minister to this person's needs?"

Because of galloping technology, "we are losing a lot of the art of medicine. I think that we physicians and health care deliverers and providers—third party or otherwise—get too wrapped up sometimes in technology and what we expect from it. We need to abide by the honored art of healing and then strengthen it with technology's ability to analyze and interpret diagnostic findings.

"We lose sight of the fact that there is another component of healing and this is hands-on time: time spent suffering with, listening to, and sharing feelings with a patient, cultivating that time to get to know the patient without a sense of haste. 'Do you not have time for me?' is a complaint we hear not infrequently from patients.

"There are some physicians who are unbelievably skilled in leaving the impression that they are never rushed and that they hear everything the patient says. This is part of the art of medicine. And for some the art still exists and they do well with their patients. For those who don't have it—or who never learned it—there are complaints from patients that their doctors never have time for them, never return telephone calls, never talk to their families. It continues to be a problem for some physicians.

"But nowadays more patients want to come in, be 'plugged' into a computer, and have the computer tell them what is wrong, what needs to be done. And to a degree, increasingly, the profession is doing just that. We lose the business of sitting down and taking the patient's medical history: 'What makes this person tick?' 'Why is his or her personality structured the way it is?' 'How long has this person really been sick?'"

Eighty-five percent of the information needed to make an accurate diagnosis, Pennell explained, is obtained by taking the patient's medical history. "And then we do the simple art of a physical exam—the touching, feeling, sharing. It's then that we determine the extent of the health needs and how to address the problems."

Patient care at the Medical Center is available in levels. "Because we virtually have every specialty under one roof," Pennell explained, "we can do these specialties as well or better than most."

Family practice is an example of the primary care level, he added, where a patient contacts a doctor who diagnoses and decides how to treat a health problem. Primary care physicians or internists who usually are generalists provide this basic broad-based medical care. If the condition is complicated or acute and if the condition warrants it, these patients are referred either to a specialist or a special medical care facility. Insurance providers usually require this "referral" process.

At the secondary level of specialized medicine, care becomes more sophisticated.

A patient in a Northwest North Carolina rural clinic can receive very good care from a local physician "where a problem is picked up," Pennell explained. "But when the physician is not absolutely sure what it is—he or she just knows that the patient's esophagus does not work properly"—then the patient is referred to a secondary or regional hospital for further evaluation and management by other experienced clinicians.

The patient, he said, can end up at the Medical Center, a tertiary provider or third level of the health care system, for a specialized diagnosis available because of its capabilities as a multidisciplinary facility providing comprehensive specialty health care.

Patients are primary beneficiaries of these three stratifications, Pennell added, "because we have services that most other institutions are not capable of rendering. And people want to get them from us."

A medical school, he continued, educates students in medicine, health, or paramedical specialties, while a hospital addresses the totality of health care delivery for those it is structured to serve, be it in preventive health, community health, public health, or health maintenance. An academic medical center brings the components together as the teaching and curative arm of medicine, he added, and for survival, it needs a highly developed research arm.

This is necessary, he recognizes, because today's patients have more complex illnesses, their treatment is far more technologically dispensed, and their hospital stays often can be longer and more involved simply because medical science recognizes that today's diseases are usually the result of multisystem illnesses or breakdowns.

"While specialized treatment is provided for an exceedingly large percentage of the patients in our Medical Center, we are still involved—and must be—in primary health care," Pennell said.

Improved technology and advanced diagnostic capabilities, he acknowledged, can retrieve some very sick people who previously got no second chances and can detect much earlier many of the current cripplers, especially cancers, often giving people additional decades of life. These same new awarenesses allow patients access to ambulatory or same-day outpatient surgery, thereby reducing health care costs, length of hospital stays, and inconveniences to patients.

Sometimes these two seem-to-be pluses are done mainly for the benefit of insurance providers who appear often to be goading health providers to make haste.

"While we try to provide care and convalescence, which is perceivably and demonstratively better, we also try to upgrade our component of prevention: prevention of hypertension; cancer of the lung, breast, cervix, and colon; atherosclerosis (hardening of the arteries); and obesity."

These prevention components brought the Medical Center fame, funds, and focus and, along with the Medical Center's accomplishments and expertise, gave birth to its guiding principle: *"When choosing the best means the most."*

The Medical Center is a recognized resource for research into heart and blood vessel disorders, cancers, health problems besieging children and the elderly, rehabilitation, human nutrition and chronic disease prevention, molecular medicine and genetics, and the neurosciences. Medical faculty physicians and scientists and their support staffs provide the credentials that help make these advancements possible.

Financial support from grants, foundations, and fellowships enables much of this research.

By July 2002, outside financial support for research and related activities at the Wake Forest University School of Medicine reached $145.6 million, a 9.6 percent increase over 2001's total of $132.8 million.

Most of these outside funds, $130.5 million, went for research and the remainder to demonstration and service projects for patients, specifically those suffering from sickle cell disease or hemophilia and for the Child Guidance Clinic and outreach educational programs.

Of the $145.6 million, 78.9 percent, was financed by the federal government—mostly from the NIH—10.8 percent from industry, and 8.1 percent from foundations and voluntary health agencies. Most medical schools are now receiving higher grant levels because Congress has drastically increased its funds to NIH. Wake Forest's portion increased from $56.2 million in 1998 to nearly $106 million in 2001.

In 2001, most of the direct outside funds went to research renewal and enlargement at the Comprehensive Cancer Center, General Research Center, and the newly formed Human Genomics Center.

The Medical Center at present ranks 35th among national academic medical centers receiving direct funding from the NIH. Nine medical school departments rank in the top 20 in the country in NIH funding for similar units nationwide. The Departments of Physiology and Pharmacology and Public Health Services rank third and fourth in the nation in total NIH research funding. The Department of Family and Community Medicine ranks 10th; the Department of Pathology, 16th; the Division of Surgical Sciences, and the Departments of Obstetrics and Gynecology, Neurology, and Anesthesiology, 18th; and the Division of Radiologic Sciences, 19th.

Research support to the medical school from the State of North Carolina reached $808,401 in 2001. The state is a major supporter of demonstration and service projects, like the Northwest Area Health Education Center (AHEC), which provides continuing education for doctors, nurses, and other health professionals in a 17-county area.

Because of this research support, Pennell explained, "We develop new techniques for medicine. Others learn from us. That way we stay ahead, that way we stay better, that way we fulfill our mission."

As an example of keeping ahead, he cited the $37 million J. Paul Sticht Center on Aging and Rehabilitation that opened in 1997.

In its "America's Best Hospitals," 2002 edition, *U.S. News and World Report* placed Baptist Hospital in the top 43 hospitals in the nation in six out of 17 specialties, starting with geriatrics, which ranks 15th in the nation. The other specialties selected were cancer, 23rd; ear, nose, and throat, 23rd; urology, 24th; heart and heart surgery, 31st; and orthopaedics, 43ʳᵈ. These same specialties made the 2001 rankings. All moved higher in their placement except for urology which held its same rating among the top 50 hospitals in the United States.

Baptist's geriatric program has been saluted before by the magazine for its Sticht Center, which provides acute care for the elderly and rehabilitation and psychiatric services for all adults. It also helps those recuperating from major illnesses and injuries to relearn the skills necessary for living.

"People over 60," Pennell explained, "usually are entering their most expensive period of health care, so 'reconditioning' medicine needs to be emphasized. Preventive health means that people need not become dependent before their time, and we can help them in this process through better care and research."

The goal of the Sticht Center is to train people to handle the special needs of the elderly and to teach them to deal with their special needs in order that they may improve their quality of life. This is necessary, Pennell realizes, "because it is not uncommon for the elderly to be afflicted with two major illnesses at one time."

The Sticht Center also is involved in geriatric research and provides legal assistance for the elderly.

Nationally, geriatrics as a new field in medicine began in 1988, but the Medical Center started its specialty in geriatric care management and adult day care services in 1987. The premise was to help the elderly cope with their medical problems while trying to remain at home with some degree of independence and goodness of living.

The Medical Center, Pennell said, meets the general needs of all people, not just the elderly, and one of CPS's duties is to see that this all-inclusive care system remains operative. Recognition of this quality of vast care is reflected in the medical school's rank among the top 50 of 125 nationally accredited medical schools and the hospital's rank as among the best nationally in the care of geriatrics, heart, urology, cancer, orthopaedics, and ear, nose and throat patients.

"Our tertiary medical center," he added, has various patient-entry levels: emergency, urgent, and routine.

"Routine admissions are handled by reservation and are scheduled electively. Urgent entries are for those people who need admittance within three days. Emergency medicine is available to patients with life-threatening illnesses who obviously have to be seen immediately.

"The percentages of the categories have remained roughly the same in recent years, although true emergency admissions are increasing due to AirCare and our expanded trauma services and that means we can, on a 24-hour basis, care for the worst of injured patients.

"To be classified as a Level One Trauma Center, we have to meet certain criteria, including operating rooms, intensive care units, and patient load capacities; physicians on-call and in-house; and the ability to do CAT scans around the clock."

The trauma center's Level One designation received a three-year certificate of renewal—without deficiencies—early in 2000, given by the North Carolina Office of Emergency Medical Services, a status it consistently has held since 1982 when it first received this distinction. The facility was defined in this latest certificate-approval report as a "showcase trauma center" for the state.

The Medical Center also was saluted for its "long-standing trauma and emergency medicine leadership" and for its commitment to a broad-based spectrum of trauma services.

The Committee on Trauma of the American College of Surgeons reverified the trauma center's repeated level of competency in June 2001. This on-site verification process, requested by the hospital, is conducted by a team of surgeons experienced in the field of trauma who determine if the hospital has met all criteria necessary for the designation. This includes 24-hour in-house availability by trauma surgeons and availability of care in specialties, such as orthopaedic surgery, neurosurgery, anesthesiology, emergency medicine, radiology, and critical care. Other capabilities include cardiac, hand, pediatric and microvascular surgery, and hemodialysis.

The Medical Center unit is now the only pediatric Level One Trauma Center in North Carolina and one of only two medical centers in the state earning the national Level One accreditation for adults.

National approval of the WFUBMC's Trauma Center, Pennell said, is even more important now that the country has experienced firsthand devastation from terrorist attacks—and threats of possible future assaults—be they biological, chemical, nuclear, or fallout from their contamination.

"Our Trauma Center team," he said, "is better prepared because its Level One status stringently requires that we be adequately prepared at any given moment. For instance, we are put on heightened alert whenever the president, vice president, and other people of note are in our area. We are the designated health care facility to take care of these officials, should they need critical expert care. Our care level extends further out into our immediate community and to those in nearby areas.

"CPS oversees the coordination of our disaster response readiness with the help of medical professionals, in-place equipment, stockpiled vaccines and supplies, protective clothing, and necessary service personnel.

"Our response will be to those brought in for care and those already in our care and for the safety of all patients and personnel. And we, like the community, could be operating with possible damage to our facilities, and with loss of electrical power, water, electronic-driven equipment, and heating and cooling abilities.

"In the past," he continued, "we learned much of our preparedness from contagious diseases, major fires, airplane and highway crashes, and natural disasters like tornadoes and hurricanes. Readiness became one of our primary obligations—CPS's forethought vigilance. For half a century now, the Medical Center has been heedful of this and looked to its chiefs to coordinate its response. Twice a year rehearsal drills keep us alert and heighten our preparedness.

"Recent terrorist attacks and hostilities against our nation made us aware of our need to expand our readiness and to recognize that we will be competing with other health care facilities for available federal and state disaster funds and antibiotic and vaccine supplies. No health care facility, for example, now has smallpox vaccine, including us. That's a national malady.

"The limiting factor will not be our ability or availability of operating rooms, X-ray facilities, laboratory equipment, or standby supplies like masks, rubber gloves, and protective clothing. None of that. That's no problem. We've met those criteria. Our limiting factor will be the same as any medical facility in the nation: lack of available critical care beds and nurses, nationwide quandaries."

Both the American medical and hospital associations, he said, are helping health care systems to fully develop major crisis medical response capabilities sufficient to address any massive casualties.

"Our contingency plans," Pennell explained, "would depend on the size and scope of disasters in our target area. With these new types of potential disasters, the resources needed to respond well may be beyond what the Medical Center—or any medical center—can provide."

The facilities and capabilities of this Medical Center, including its public health oversight, would not be the only ones inundated by disasters, he said. Medical teams in nearby locations, such as armed service personnel, would be swamped at their locations.

"We are better off than a lot of places," Pennell said, "and I think we are far better prepared than most. Confronted with the unimaginable," he added, "we would do whatever is necessary to respond to any eventuality. Our facilities are in the best condition they ever have been, but I cannot overemphasize our bed-space limitations. You can have the best anesthesiologists, best surgeons, best antibiotics, and everything else, but if you don't have a place to take care of patients, you cannot fully respond. However, our professionals are well trained and knowledgeable of what would be required of them, should we be involved in national or area disasters."

Over 59,000 visits are handled annually by the Medical Center's Emergency Department, Pennell said, showing the heavy use of this $57 million building completed in 1996 and the extent of this specialty care. Its patient load is rising at a rate of about 5 percent a year compared to 2 percent nationally, he added.

"What this country learned in the Vietnam War, as to the capabilities of helicopter transportation, led to the development of AirCare, our air-ambulance emergency service, another arm of the Emergency Department's quality care," Pennell said.

"The Emergency Department, as currently structured, is set up to take care of people who become ill suddenly or are victims of accidents and trauma. People trained in this relatively new discipline increasingly are becoming extremely capable.

"Here and everywhere, there has been a problem with its abuse: nonemergency use, or substituting it for a regular physician or no physician, or regarding it as an all-night clinic. However, this misuse is subsiding because people are now better educated about health care. Also, more people are educated about what an Emergency Department is and how to use it. They learn that they may have to pay out-of-pocket if not precertified by their insurance companies.

"The Emergency Department is the most expensive route an individual can go for medical treatment. And, in turn, it becomes a problem for the institution because many of the people who seek this method of health care are medical indigents: They have no on-going continuity of health care delivery, so they come to the Emergency Department. And often, the hospital gets stuck with their bills.

"And there are those situations where the system often bogs down because nonemergencies take up space, facilities, and everything else—much like the crunch that takes place when AirCare comes in with true emergencies.

"But the not-truly-emergency service is one we have to render. The people involved in emergency medicine recognize this, and they accept it admirably.

"In true emergencies, we never ask about finances. There are those who do not like being asked up front for insurance numbers and information. They think we are only interested in getting paid, and, as the result, we sometimes get a black eye.

"No place in the Medical Center is under more scrutiny by the public than this arena of urgency medicine. Anyone who walks into the

Emergency Department, other than those in life-threatening situations, and takes up an hour or more of a doctor's time ought to be willing to pay for that service—just as they would pay their private physician.

"Some Emergency Department patients complain that no doctors—only nurses—are present and involved. We need to educate the public on this: This is not happenstance medicine. There are on-duty faculty physicians—specialists—who practice and teach crisis medicine and who are acquainted with pressure decisions and life-and-death circumstances. Fully licensed physicians who are residents assist.

"We triage patients according to their needs. Doctors may not immediately be visible because they are handling patients in different parts of the Emergency Department, or they are involved with studies, X-rays, CAT scans, fractures, or the transfer of patients from emergency to various intensive care units for treatment.

"On-duty nurses are as qualified as physicians to handle much of the entry-level care. Nurses in the emergency room must have special temperaments, special training, and firsthand experience in emergency care. They serve as effective team members with the physician staff and in calming patients and their families who often arrive in acute states of anxiety.

"Only about 20 percent of the patients seen in the Emergency Department are trauma cases. Injuries are trauma. They don't have to be massive to belong to that category. Mash your finger and it is a trauma. Stick yourself with a pin and that is a trauma. Big trauma means multi-system injuries."

The Emergency Department serves two purposes: one section for urgent-care and after-hours quasi-emergency care and the other solely for the crisis-to-trauma emergency cases. The department is located within sight of Business Interstate 40 and next door to AirCare's helicopter landing pad, so it is easily accessible.

AirCare flies a Bell 412 helicopter, considered the most proven airframe for medical transport in the world. Its pilots are instrument qualified and receive regular and ongoing training and test-flight experience. Flight nurses are certified in air ambulance patient care. AirCare is the only one of six hospital-based programs in the state currently flying with both a pilot and copilot on board on a 24-hour instrument flight rules basis. There are 200 hospital-based air ambulance programs in the nation.

Baptist Hospital entered into a lease program with Air Method Corporation International in 1986 to operate AirCare. No ambulance flights are undertaken without pilot-only determination that weather or other conditions are conducive to safe flight. Pilots are not informed of

Dr. Eben Alexander, a neurosurgeon, was the first Chief of Professional Services (CPS) at Wake Forest University Baptist Medical Center. He served from 1953 to 1973. His hallmark was excellence in patient care.

Now retired, Dr. Alexander continues a vigil over N.C. Baptist Hospital and Wake Forest University School of Medicine from the Emeritus House, his weekday home, where he writes articles on neurosurgery.

B

Dr. Thomas H. Irving served as the second Chief of Professional Services from 1973 to 1977 and was known as a master facilitator. He served as the first chairman of the Department of Anesthesia from 1969 to 1982.

Dr. Robert N. Headley, third CPS (1977-1981), was head of the Section on Cardiology. Adept at understanding Baptist Hospital's finances, he helped to establish its capital equipment budget fund.

Dr. Courtland H. Davis Jr., a neurosurgeon, was the fourth chief (1982-1986). He led CPS when decisions were made to add ambulatory and same-day surgery, the air ambulance service, and lithotripter equipment.

E

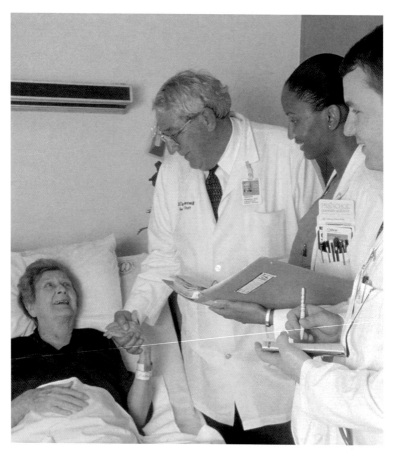

Dr. Timothy C. Pennell, a general surgeon and professor of surgical sciences, served four years on the executive committee of the CPS and then as the fifth chief from 1986 to 2000 for a total of 18 years.

Dr. Pennell directed the Office of International Health Affairs (1982-2000) for the Medical Center and was the first graduate of Wake Forest University School of Medicine to be named as Chief of Professional Services.

Dr. Vardaman M. Buckalew Jr. became the sixth, and current, Chief of Professional Services in July 2000. A nephrologist, he is a professor of Nephrology and of Physiology and Pharmacology.

—*Photos courtesy of Biomedical Communications,*
Wake Forest University Baptist Medical Center

H

a patient's medical condition in order to preserve the integrity of the "to-fly" decision. Most patients transported by AirCare are admitted to one of the hospital's intensive care units.

AirCare, aware of a new need to serve the perilously ill, now has a Critical Care Ground Transport Unit (CCT), Pennell said. It is dubbed as the Medical Center's "ICU on wheels." It picks up patients within a 100-mile radius of Winston-Salem, but it is not competitive with local Emergency Medical Service (EMS). Its staff, as with AirCare, is trained in emergency advanced lifesaving medicine, allowing its staff to monitor and treat a variety of patients en route to the Medical Center.

Another notable assistance offered by the Emergency Department, Pennell added, is its new nursing service for victims of domestic violence, sexual assault, and child abuse. These victims are treated with compassion, comfort, and privacy. The goal is to provide a sheltered environment that protects patients' dignity, he added. Forensic-trained nurse examiners, who collect evidence for possible criminal prosecution, perform physical exams in protected and private examining rooms, and administer treatment, directed by examining physicians or physician assistants. A nearby, and also private, conference room is available for law enforcement officials to take statements from victims.

Just as there are patient-entry levels, Pennell said, there are hospital care levels, also under CPS's scrutiny.

A general hospital, he defined, provides services for most patients' illnesses. A specialized hospital cares for those whose illnesses are beyond routine. Rehabilitation hospitals provide services to help patients adjust to mental and physical disabilities brought on by illnesses. Research hospitals conduct medical research. And teaching hospitals educate future physicians, nurses, specialists, and other health caregivers.

The Medical Center, Pennell said, provides care at all of these five major levels—and more—because of its comprehensive makeup as an academic medical center with a teaching hospital, "and that is what distinguishes us from other medical centers. Charlotte Medical Center, for example, is a teaching hospital," Pennell explained, "but it is not an academic medical center because it does not have a medical school. Forsyth calls itself a medical center, and indeed they are, but they are not an academic medical center. It is a teaching medical center because some of our medical students rotate over there, but they are *our* students."

The WFU medical school has 767 full-time faculty members—538 clinical, 189 basic science, 40 others, and 3,501 administration and support staff for a total of 4,268. WFUP has a full-time staff of 486 board-certified doctors representing over 85 medical and surgical specialties and subspecialties in its clinical practice and outpatient clinics. They also serve as the attending staff for the hospital.

Baptist Hospital has 1,549 registered nurses, 482 licensed practical nurses and nursing assistants, 934 clinical professionals, 537 house officers, and 3,351 administrative and support staff for a total workforce of 6,853.

It was Dr. Meads, Pennell explained, who was the first, back in the 1960s, to go to local community leaders "and point out what a gold mine they had within the city limits: an academic medical center with unbelievable facilities and capabilities. Many didn't realize then just what Baptist Hospital was doing up there on the Hill—especially with its care of indigent patients. It didn't take long for the community, thanks to Manson Meads, to pick up on this."

Today, he added, those now serving the Medical Center and all its subsidiaries total 11,121, "making it the leading employer in Forsyth County and providing absolutely the best health care available in the region. And I would hope our spirit of compassion and Judeo-Christian heritage over the years has rubbed off onto other industries, businesses, and groups in the community.

"Our involvement in the community," Pennell explained, "goes beyond health care." He cited as examples, "our cash infusion into Winston-Salem's economy, our growing research emphasis, and our leadership and partnership in the development of a community-based biotechnology center in downtown Winston-Salem, the Piedmont Triad Research Park, in which companies are beginning to cluster."

The overall staff of the Office for Chief of Professional Services, Pennell said, maintains the vigil that safeguards all of the services and all of the staff at all of the levels and in all of the enterprises found at the Medical Center.

XI MEDICAL INTERVENTION TRAVELS
MANY ROUTES

Medicine is a rapidly developing phenomenon—except for those yearning for miracles. They fear they never will embrace a season of restitution.

Medicine's earlier quantum leaps—sanitation, antibiotics, and surgery, to name just three—gave patients hope. That same hope is alive at the Medical Center, for CPS in its role of lifekeeper is very watchful that quantum leaps in health care are still in progress.

So as the mind develops, so does the profession. Medical discoveries are like crossword puzzles: The mind builds on what it knows and what it can uncover. Sometimes miracles unfold when one panacea in common practice is used as a remedy for other ills or difficulties—like common aspirin, now more than a pain reliever.

As medicine developed, so did regulating groups, including the American Medical Association, the Association of American Medical Colleges (AAMC), the Accrediting Council for Graduate Medical Education, the American Board of Medical Specialties, the American Hospital Association, and the Joint Commission on Accreditation of Healthcare Organizations. They were organized to elevate and maintain standards so that no harm would be done to patients who seek professional help. Their advent caused medical schools to associate with either hospitals for clinical training or with universities for scholarly accreditation, or to create academic medical centers combining all of them.

WFUBMC has all of these components: education, training, healing, and research. It adheres to these basic regulatory groups, and many others, as it endeavors under CPS's interpretation to remain a superior host for healing.

The hospital's regulatory groups—Hospital Licensing for North Carolina, JCAHO, and Medicare/Medicaid—require it to have a leadership group for its organized medical staff and services rendered. The Office for Chief of Professional Services fulfills these requirements.

The Medical Center, Pennell said, "is in the top one-third among the academic medical centers in the nation as defined by grant dollars, specifically NIH money. I think we can move up, but I do not think we ought to aspire to be in the top 10, maybe not even the top 20. For when one does, then it totally changes the complexion of the institution because everything then becomes research based. That would mean that all we do would be based on research and our patient care would suffer. We are medically oriented here, so our first commitments are to patient care and medical education."

NIH is an agency of the Public Health Service of the U.S. Department of Health and Human Services. It conducts and supports a wide range of biomedical research, provides funds for training research scientists, and finances about 40 percent of all health resources and development in America. In its own laboratories, it deals with major areas, including aging, infectious diseases, arthritis, skin diseases, cancer, child health and human development, diabetes and digestive and kidney diseases, neurological disorders and stroke, and heart, lungs, and blood—and in 2001 the addition of mind-body interaction on human health and disease.

These same areas of research are dealt with—as well as others—at the medical school, Pennell said. "Each department has its own research and development funds, which are governed by rigid policies. Each department pays what is called the dean's tax—that's money to run the school and to support the school's academic endeavors.

"We teach medical students anatomy," the study in detail of the body's structures and organs through analysis, dissection, and physiology. "It is easier to get grant money to address cancer treatment, pathophysiology, molecular biology, and that type of program, so there are some components that the medical school will just have to pay for. Teaching anatomy and other basic sciences are the key ones," Pennell explained, "for the medical school has that responsibility. They are basic essentials in the education of medical students, and these are, after all, our future doctors.

"Our role in education," Pennell emphasized, "is especially for medical students, and that is the one thing that makes us different as an academic teaching medical center. But our other aspects of education are important, too."

Other training programs are provided for residents; physician assistants, technicians and laboratory scientists and workers; graduate students in each of the medical school's biomedical sciences and all its medical departments and specialties; and physicians, residents, registered nurses, pharmacists, and their assistants in continuing education.

"The government must carry a significant responsibility for research either through NIH agencies or grants. It is the researcher who studies the body, how it functions, how disease can impair it, and how disease and damage to the human body can be corrected," Pennell said.

A researcher, he defined, may be a clinical scientist who looks for answers in her or his given field of medicine and from patients, or a researcher may be a basic scientist whose quest is primarily pursued in the laboratory.

In the future, Pennell said, "research has to be funded from a multitude of sources. The government, obviously, must carry a significant responsibility, but increasingly private industries, such as pharmaceutical companies and manufacturers of medical equipment, will need to help underwrite the cost.

"We need money for research and even more space for research, but we are fortunate to have the basic scientists, faculty, and research components that we do."

Financial support for research keeps rising, Pennell explained, and this is confirmation that the Medical Center's biomedical discoveries and creative alternatives enable more patients to recover. This support, he said, allows the spawning and enlarging of services and educational opportunities that benefit those seeking medical help. There is no way, he added, to put a total on unsolicited support from within the Medical Center.

People may question the dollar support for research, Pennell said, but medicine needs it, for it is a main branch of the profession, and "a good physician is constantly calling on research. We look to those whose job and responsibility it is to do research and to develop new concepts and techniques. Those in the middle of clinical practice need to collaborate with our research scientists so that we can ask, 'Is this combination of drugs better for this type of cancer than that combination of drugs?' For those of us in academics, it is a constant mesh of both researcher and physician.

"We must keep contributing, questioning, wondering, and looking anew repeatedly at the way we practice medical intervention, healing, and research."

Medicine's goal, generally speaking, "is to make people live longer and live better, and nowhere is that more true today than in the treatment and care of patients with heart disease, cancer, trauma, and infectious diseases. I think for a period of time there is an improved quality of life. I wish I could say that for all those who come to us for help and hope."

Of all the cures and advancements, Pennell said, speaking personally, "I would like to see cancer heading the list, followed by diabetes, heart diseases, atherosclerosis, mental illness. The list goes on and on.

"Another is trauma prevention. Improvement of trauma care over the past couple of decades has been staggering. That has to continue.

The greatest imperative we have in our society is preventing trauma: educating people about the dangers of chainsaws, increasing high speeds on the highways, not wearing seatbelts, carrying guns, television violence and its impact on society, lack of safety in the workplace, and no education on peaceful resolution as opposed to conflict and violent resolution.

"Trauma carepersons have got to be involved in this prevention as well as society, for we must realize that we have a terrible disease upon our hands. Some of it may well be related to addiction problems, such as thefts and shootings, robberies, stabbings—those times when individuals arrive at a point where they will do anything to feed their habit. This is, as are many illnesses, a multipronged issue."

But then, Pennell said, speaking as a surgeon, "I think you can help everybody. There's a difference between 'help' and 'cure.' But what many patients want is a miracle: immediate attention and immediate cure. If it involves surgery, they want less invasive procedures, less hassle, less inconvenience, less cost, and quick recovery."

Doctors, regardless of specialty, "spend more of their time in treatment than diagnosis. Inpatient care is the most time consuming. It's also the most cost consuming. The more critical the care, the more time and cost consuming it is. High-tech costs."

The high expenditure for advancements in operating, maintaining, and expanding the academic medical complex began in renewed and earnest over 41 years ago when Medical Center leaders began to assess how to better respond to patients' wants, especially in the Piedmont with its societal combination of agriculture and high-stress industries.

The medical school was faced with students clamoring for entrance, causing the faculty to expand along with the curriculum.

The hospital was faced with a heightened demand for inpatient care in every field, forcing it to enlarge its capabilities, treatment possibilities, and medical staff specialists.

Biomedical researchers were faced with finding answers to deep-seated medical enigmas as science began to seek and find ways to understand the cause and effect of disease on the human body.

The time was ripe for this academic medical center, the 69th in the nation when it was begun, to cure its own deficiencies, to double its space for patient care and research.

So the "The Miracle on Hawthorne Hill" again took bold steps toward a bold future.

In the decade of the 1990s, renewed dedication toward quality brought about further building, renovation of use-worn structures, and birth of new specialties.

It was a manifestation of the Medical Center's core mission to society, adopted in 1973. It committed itself, within the limits of its resources, to four goals: superior education for students and teachers of health professionals, continuum patient care emphasizing human dignity based on Judeo-Christian principles, discoveries and application of new knowledge in basic and clinical research in the biomedical sciences, and progressive participation in improving health care delivery systems wherever dispensed in the world.

The growing and enlarging has not stopped. Constant construction sounds give evidence that this house of medical safekeeping is responding to its calling.

What Medical Center leaders learned from their giant step into geriatrics in the 1940s led to further care for the elderly with the 1993 addition of The Nursing Center at Oak Summit, a skilled and intermediate nursing care facility 10 miles away, and with the 1994 addition of the Sticht Center, a stand-alone geriatric facility on the main campus.

The Geriatric Research Center at Wake Forest University, now located in Sticht, is one of only 10 national research sites—it started as the third in the nation and the first in the state—to be designated as a Claude D. Pepper Older Americans Independence Center. A Pepper Center since 1991, it consistently is saluted for its research on preventing disabilities and maintaining the independence of older Americans. Two of its current studies are looking into how exercise and weight loss can reduce pain and disability associated with osteoarthritis of the knee and the value of cardiac rehabilitation in treating patients with heart disease.

The National Institute on Aging funds both the Sticht and Pepper centers.

Medicine's life-extenders allow the elderly to live longer, and the Medical Center wants these gifts of time to be more truly golden.

Aging elders occupy more of physicians' patient load, Pennell reported, "and they occupy more of the health care dollars and health care beds. And this is going to increase as life expectancy extends and the baby boomers—those born since the late 1940s—reach 65 and older."

Because of the increase of the elderly receiving care at the Medical Center, Pennell said, "we have acute care designated specifically for older patients and their health improvement. Rather than bringing them into the classic hospital setting, it is a geriatric setting."

Any specialty care—age not being relevant—is more expensive, he added, simply because of the more intensified and individualized care by specialists.

Often, he continued, "those patients complaining the most about the cost are the ones who want all the tests. And that's a real dilemma. A patient gets a headache or has a headache for an extended period, so he or she asks, 'Is a brain tumor causing this headache?' The likelihood of a brain tumor causing it is not great, but the best way to determine this is by ordering an MRI, an extremely costly test.

"Or patients come in with abdominal pain. They've had good workups elsewhere, but we end up getting a CAT scan on them when we know there is nothing wrong. It is probably a stress- or tension-related pain or what have you. That creates a real problem for us. There are times when we spend unnecessary money just to answer patients' questions. The CAT scan and MRI are two tests where this is especially true."

As for cost, Pennell said, the hospital has designated staff to work with people who have no insurance or who have only Medicare or Medicaid. About a half of the uninsured eventually pay their bills, he said. Others live under the mistaken idea that the hospital will take away their homes and all they own if they do not settle their bills.

Because it is Baptist-related, some people think they should get full and free service from the hospital. This, of course, is neither true nor possible. The services are delivered with Judeo-Christian concerns, but patients are still responsible for their debts.

When the hospital was chartered by the Baptists in North Carolina in 1922, its purpose, Pennell said, was to "receive and treat patients either free or for compensation." Over the years the hospital has rendered care to indigent patients as it was considered an integral part of its ministry. Funds for this care are provided through the Baptist State Convention's annual Mother's Day Fund, by Baptist churches being solicited by the hospital for direct gifts, and by other patient endowment gifts. While the totality of this support is significant and vital, it does not cover the total cost of the free care provided.

The hospital provides free care to patients unable to pay under guidelines determined by its financial counseling division and annually updated poverty guidelines as established by the U.S. Department of Health and Human Services.

"I think both institutions have been very, very good at finding other funding for patients who do not have it, either through vocational rehabilitation, cancer support, or some other organizations like that," Pennell said.

Baptist Hospital annually makes over $170 million in contractual adjustments with patients and insurance providers and gives about $52 million in free care.

To be more cost-efficient, Baptist has same-day surgical units where patients go into the hospital early in the morning and return home in the early evening. Today about half of the surgical operations performed at Baptist are on outpatients who go to the Day Hospital for uncomplicated procedures. Insurance companies press for this quick turnaround surgery as a way to reduce costs.

Having to discharge patients faster, however, does not mean patients do not receive the care they need.

Advanced technology allows them to stay hospitalized for shorter periods and in a seamless manner to receive much of their post-hospital care safely at home, Pennell said. "This is made possible by the hospital's home care services, where nurses and therapists go to patients' homes, making sure they are taking their medications, getting their dressings changed, doing their physical therapy, and giving them their IVs, where necessary. Here we have somebody checking on them and that's different from anything we've had in the past.

"We've had this program in place for over 10 years, but it has taken off significantly recently because unequivocally it is needed. This service will expand. There is a lot of competition in this arena because Medicare, Medicaid, and private insurance programs often endorse and support it, figuring it will decrease the cost of medical care, and indeed it does."

Modern medical wonders make "revolving-door surgery" possible, such as the development of sophisticated endoscopic procedures and fiber-optic surgery, Pennell explained. It used to be that the problem was getting to a site to fix a dilemma. Now noninvasive surgery allows easier repair. Patients can go home almost immediately, are up and around in a few days, and experience less pain and suffering.

In-hospital care always will be necessary, Pennell said, so the Medical Center continues to focus, as does CPS, on how to better meet and serve patients' demands.

Brenner Children's Hospital is a fine example of compassion addressing need, he illustrated. This "hospital within a hospital" opened in 1986 to serve critically ill children and those with complex medical problems. The field has so diversified that Brenner Children's Hospital followed a nationwide trend by hospitals to devote designated units to children's medical needs, specialized care, and services. In April 2002, Brenner Children's Hospital opened an enlarged $132 million hospital in Ardmore Tower West, occupying six of its 11 floors—plus a rooftop garden activity deck. The new facility makes it possible for its 75 pediatric specialists—representing every specialty in pediatric medicine today—to provide services with the latest in technology, research, and treatment. Its patients come from the surrounding area and states. Now it can offer single room occupancy for pediatric patients and their families, offer assistance through its family resource centers, and provide a day care program for children with disabilities, giving parents respite time.

Other centers of excellence exist at the Medical Center for health problems that know no age, those that ungraciously disable the body.

Its research thrust is entering a new season of discovery befitting this new millennium and befitting its continuum of health betterment.

The Medical Center remains an eager enabler.

XII   A LIVABLE LIFE

Physicians can feel for their patients, for they can see—and must ultimately address—the devastation caused when disease corrupts the body.

They may not be able fully to feel that devastation unless they, too, have stood at life's door to transience. But in time, as companions with their patients, together they hope to experience renewal.

What makes physicians different from many other decision makers is that they promised at graduation to see patients as sacred, redeemable, and perishable. With each day and with each patient, they can seize the opportunity to halt disease's wickedness.

After all, patients are seeking what they, too, desire: a livable life.

Physicians can never assure more than they can perform, Pennell said, but at this time physicians can offer more hope, for they now can be better curators.

What physicians need from patients, Pennell added, is their vow to be better caretakers. That role begins long before patients enter medical waiting rooms asking for relief when their bodies get out of order. Better health begins with primary prevention by patients and secondary prevention by physicians who can detect diseases earlier now and get patients to the right doctors and treatments sooner.

Prevention, Pennell said, basically means adopting a lifestyle that incorporates better exercise, nutrition, weight control, rest, and mental well-being as well as no tobacco, limited alcohol, and reduced stress. In time, he said, physicians will know more about the role genetics play in diseases, perhaps making intervention possible even earlier.

Meanwhile, he continued, "part of the art of medicine—and you cannot practice medicine just as art without having the scientific basis—consists of knowing what to ask, what to look for, and tying it all together. That is art as well as science.

"The art of medicine and surgery, as far as I am concerned, goes beyond just the technical gathering and assessment of information. It has to do with the laying on of hands, assessing patients' personalities, interacting with patients, explaining in language patients can understand, and treating them with dignity.

"Part of that art is being able to tell people they have terminal cancer, being able to deal with their questions on how long they have to live, being there for them—all the while instilling confidence in them and not scaring them to death even though they have terrible things confronting them. I have yet to see a patient—who was in any way coherent—who did not want the reassurance that you were going to be with them 'all the way.' Nondesertion is important."

Pennell went into surgery "because it was dynamic and rewarding. In general surgery you have to be broadly trained and that interested me. Surgery sometimes can be mutilating but at other times lifesaving, so there is a trade-off there.

"Early on I realized that I would be happy in virtually any of the specialties, but I came to realize it was surgery I really wanted.

"One of the most challenging things about general surgery," he recalled, "is that you often are forced to be innovative and creative. You have to handle problems that you have never encountered. You have to devise your own techniques to reclaim what has been destroyed by trauma or illness or you have to perfect some surgical procedure to remove disease.

"In the process, you are taking basic surgical principles and saying, 'Yes, that will work;' 'No, that will not;' or 'This is a better system for doing that.' You could call it research-on-demand, for it may never have been done. Your goal is to save the life and allow the person to experience life in whatever measures are possible.

"That is surgery. It means learning something new every day, and that helps you to maintain a stance of humility.

"General surgery is the skin and its contents. I was principally interested in gastrointestinal surgery or the GI tract (stomach and intestines) with a special interest in biliary tract surgery, the esophagus, and the breast.

"As it relates to the breast, I think I was selected. As it relates to the esophagus, I selected it. Interests in other areas of general surgery evolved. The esophagus is an intriguing organ, difficult to work on, challenging, unforgiving. You cannot make any errors with the esophagus. The first chairman of our Department of Surgery always said that 'God did not intend for the esophagus to be operated on because of where He put it'—down the middle of the chest. Because it does not have a serosa (membrane covering), it takes more delicate and more meticulous handling and suturing techniques."

Surgery, he emphasized, is not always the instrument for relief.

"There are complications with leukemia, for example, in which surgery must be used for perforation of the gut or for inserting catheters in order to get chemotherapy into a patient, but you cannot 'operate' on leukemia.

"Even in cancer of the breast—looked upon as a surgical disease—there are those of us who feel that this is a systemic disease. Surgery can be curative at certain stages, and one of these days, we hope, there will be a nonsurgical cure for cancer of the breast. And there will be.

"There are other diseases where surgery clearly is the only cure. Hernia is an example. There are certain cancers that are best managed by total local excision, such as taking out the colon or stomach or esophagus or a portion of them.

"And there are some diseases which are much more surgical than people realize, such as ulcerative colitis. By taking out the colon, you cure that disease, but there are a lot of people who drag their feet until there are all kinds of complications—both from management or for treatment. Had the disease been addressed earlier, some of the complications could have been prevented."

To ward off colon cancer, Pennell advocates screenings using a fiber-optic flexible tube to look at the large intestines either by a sigmoidoscopy or a colonoscopy, which is far more effective of the two as it views the entire colon. If precancerous tumors are detected, they can be removed before they develop into deadly polyps.

"Surgery may not always cure, but surgery does cure and correct an awful lot of diseases. And one of the rewarding components of surgery is that it usually does so rapidly," he added.

Except in cases of trauma, Pennell said, surgery usually is not entered into hurriedly. Some patients, when informed of their illnesses, can misinterpret delay. "A woman with a lesion in her breast comes in for medical attention. It proves to be cancer. Today there is more than one way to treat cancer of the breast. We commonly practice breast preservation. I advocate it in appropriate and selected patients. I tell them: 'I want you to understand, upfront, that we are going to take our time establishing what the final diagnosis is—should it prove to be cancer. We are going to do a lot of extra studies to determine what type it is because now we are able to do more than a mastectomy, which is an acceptable treatment, but we first must get all the information together.'"

Once fortified with substantial answers from certified tests, type indentification, and treatment possibilities, Pennell continued, surgeons must help patients and spouses deal realistically with the information and ultimately the decisions on what treatment paths are to be followed.

"The appropriate decisions are not only medical and legal ones but also ethical ones: 'What is best for these patients?' I think that the

Golden Rule very adequately applies here. In most situations, there are clear-cut indications—learned from medical and surgical education, experience, and judgment—that surgery needs to be done.

"One of surgery's greatest difficulties is not *whether* to operate but *when*. When I came into surgery, there was an old adage: 'Never let the sun set or rise on an intestinal obstruction.' In other words, this is an emergency: Do it *now*.

"We have learned that patients are better off and do better—as long as the intestines are viable or living—if we get some fluids into them, resuscitate them, get their blood volume up, and get them prepared for surgery. This may take one hour or two, one day or two, one week. This is where judgment comes in. And that has bearing on both morbidity and mortality.

"With all of medicine's advancements and tools to help with presurgical diagnoses, surgeons can still be surprised upon entry into a site. It happens and it will continue to happen. One of the most common examples is when you operate on somebody for appendicitis, which basically is a clinical diagnosis. You examine a patient, and you arrive at a decision—on the basis of clinical findings without X-rays or much other laboratory work—that this patient does or does not have appendicitis.

"The patient does not sense the agony you are going through as you make your decision. You will not fully know until you are in there whether this is pelvic inflammatory disease, a ruptured ovarian cyst, Meckel's diverticulitis, or acute appendicitis. Then you may get in and find it is not appendicitis but a complicated inflammatory bowel disease or cancer or something like that.

"Improved technology has decreased the number of surprises in diseases that we deal with or encounter, including colon, gallbladder, and pancreatic diseases. But there are still those diseases and problems that may be a surprise."

Treatment and surgery have other roles in the health process, Pennell said.

"There are those forms of chemotherapy that unequivocally cure patients. There are other forms of chemotherapy that do not cure but provide an extended period of quality life or quality time.

"There are some disease processes, for instance, in which chemotherapy will not extend the remaining days, but, in fact, will make patients more miserable. Here again, it requires judgment calls by physicians, and I think most physicians do this with families and patients. Again, this is treating patients totally: physically, mentally, and spiritually."

Many intensive types of surgery, usually on trauma patients, are done by a team, Pennell said. While he may have been the surgeon, Pennell, like all physicians, had residents and faculty members to help, when needed. "Being in the operating room pumped me up with adrenaline. That is why you can sustain the long hours. After a very long operation, you felt exhausted—but also exhilarated, if it went well.

"There are very few things I dislike about surgery—maybe the long hours at times. The demand for rapid change in thought and procedures or shifting gears—going from a breast to a liver to a stomach or a colon, all in the course of one day—is hard but also very rewarding."

In surgery, he emphasized, "nothing must be routine. There are always variations. That's why it takes time to get all the training so that you have a base, a fund of knowledge, from which to draw when dealing with the variations. When you encounter unpredictables, you use your acquired knowledge to figure out what needs to be done" in the best interest of the patients.

"Patients have great difficulty accepting poor outcomes, especially when there is no way to improve their condition. But you have to try everything you can—beyond comfort care. You *have* to try."

The leading illnesses, he explained, continue to be cancer and heart problems, followed by strokes, pulmonary and infectious diseases, trauma, and dementia. Despite medicine's immense progress, Pennell said, patients still fear being told they have one of these major illnesses. Physicians today, he added, often can stave off the death-sentence conclusion patients associate with trauma illnesses, for intervention has become a scientific wonder.

For example, he said, the Medical Center keeps upgrading its ongoing fight against cancer—that insidious disease that knows every pathway within the body and loves to stretch out its tendrils to corrupt susceptible cells' growth patterns. "While an absolute cure of cancer is not always possible," he allowed, "remission, suppression, control, and intervals of disease-free states are."

The Medical Center has a long history in cancer prevention and treatment, Pennell said. In 1957, it became the first in North Carolina to use radioactive cobalt—the source most often used in X-ray treatment of cancer—on its patients.

Cancer treatment requires curators from many of medicine's family of disciplines to form the lifesaving-support teams, Pennell added, and this approach is a long-standing and ever-so-important protocol followed at the Medical Center. It will take even more cooperative efforts by researchers, radiologists, geneticists, or oncologists to suffocate the disease and lead patients once again toward hope and survivorship, he added.

One area that Pennell feels is very promising has to do with "the unique blood supply of cancer, the blood by which it gets its oxygen and nutrients, and how to alter that. It's called angiogenesis," growing new blood vessels to bypass diseased cells and snuffing out their essential blood supply. The treatment's goal when fully developed would starve tumors, killing only cancerous cells, and blocking their spread.

And with the current worldwide study of genomics, Pennell said, more light will be shone on cancer's rage against the body and more light switches will be developed to turn off the multiplying of deformed cells. In the past, physicians treated the 200 known types of cancer either by surgery, radiation, or chemotherapy, destroying sick and well cells. Now scientists are learning from the current gene study that most cancers are caused either from inherited genetic defects or from a lifetime of sunbathing or smoking. New drugs are now being designed to target and kill only tumor cells, letting patients bypass the side effects of nausea, fatigue, and hair loss confronted in regular therapy. A vaccine using molecular biology techniques now in early clinical trials is showing signs of stopping some cancers and halting further advancement of some tumors.

"When I entered medicine," Pennell recalled, "certain segments of society didn't talk about cancer of the rectum or cancer of the uterus, testicles, breast, or prostate. That was kept in the closet. It is better now, but it needs to be confronted even more openly—for the patient's sake! We cannot overemphasize the importance of screening and early detection."

Basic science and clinical cancer researchers at the Medical Center are involved in national clinical research studies that are leading the way to improving therapy treatments, patient outcomes, and diagnostic procedures for early detection and prevention and hopefully a cure.

They will be aided, Pennell said, by secrets uncovered from DNA studies and other noninvasive techniques, and better lymph node mapping along with early detection, all features of cancer prevention and treatment practiced at the Medical Center.

The National Cancer Institute (NCI) in 1972 recognized Wake Forest University's national leadership in cancer care and research, naming it a Specialized Clinical Cancer Research Center. In 1990, Pennell added, NCI designated it as a Comprehensive Cancer Center (CCC) for being among the best treatment facilities in the country, a high reward for the collaborative efforts made by the leadership of the medical school and hospital.

Today it is one of only 38 Comprehensive Cancer Centers in the nation and the only one in Western North Carolina. This seal of approval means the Medical Center is active at the forefront of progressive cancer treatment, education, and research, offering its patients a wide array of options to reduce the violence of the disease.

While the Section of Oncology initiated the establishment of the cancer center, it is now directed by its Department of Cancer Biology, Pennell explained. CPS, which endorsed its creation, continues to monitor its clinical activities in matters that relate to the precautionary welfare of its patients.

To further enlarge and empower its 30-year commitment to the eradication of cancer, the Medical Center is building a $75 million Outpatient Comprehensive Cancer Center on its main campus. Here all the existing outpatient oncology services will be integrated into a four-story, 257,350-square-foot facility on the northwest side of the Medical Center across from the Emergency Department. Completion is expected by the summer of 2003.

The center will include the radiation oncology department and outpatient oncology pharmacy, a personal appearance center, the Cancer Registry, a cancer patient support program, a meditation room, food court, and administrative offices. The medical oncology clinic space will include a lung cancer clinic and a multidisciplinary genitourinary clinic, the clinical research management program, and the outpatient clinical laboratory. The outpatient radiology department and surgical oncology clinic area will include the Breast Care Center and a head and neck cancer clinic.

At present, these various aspects of oncology services are strewn across the campus, making it tiresome, first of all, for sick patients to traipse from physician to oncologist, to X-ray, to chemotherapy and radiation treatment, to labs, and to get drugs. And secondly, it is now difficult for physicians and other caregivers whose offices are not connected to collaborate on treatment modalities and thus serve their patients more effectively and efficiently. And, thirdly, there is no more room currently for physician offices, treatment areas, and multidisciplinary clinics to expand or to increase staff, or enlarge for the addition of new equipment needed for several years.

The new building will have planned zoning, the current approach in medicine: regionalizing its full range of care services by clinical specialty. This helps patients get all of their care, treatment, and therapy in a centralized location, making their visits more comfortable, in more attractive facilities, and less stressful for them and their physicians.

It is an approach the Medical Center is incorporating in all future buildings and in the reconditioning of old facilities. The new cancer center also will be designed so that it can grow as needed in the future.

Other hospitals in the area have one-unit cancer centers, Pennell said, but none in the region will be as large, as comprehensive, as multidisciplined, or as advanced in full-range capabilities as this one. This center will still have access to clinical trials and research already being done by Medical Center scientists.

"It is essential," Pennell said, "that the Medical Center provide this enlarged, more coordinated and correlated outpatient Comprehensive Cancer Center for its patients. It provides absolutely the very best in cancer treatment, research, protocol, care, and cure. In its new home, the cancer center can only become better and more comprehensive."

As an NCI-designated comprehensive cancer center, the Medical Center participates in basic research, clinical trials, community outreach, and prevention programs. Research is underway to reduce the incidence of graft versus host disease, to prevent infection, and to accelerate the recovery of bone marrow after transplant.

The Medical Center established its bone marrow transplant program in 1990. The National Marrow Donor Program approved it as a transplant center in 1994 and as a collection center in 1991. It is the national program's second largest collection center in America.

This center is one of only 76 programs in the country accredited for autologous and allogeneic bone marrow and peripheral blood progenitor cell transplantation. In autologous transplantation, the patient's own bone marrow or stem cells are used; and in allogeneic surgery, stem cells from either related or unrelated donors are inserted.

The bone marrow transplant center received a three-year accreditation from the Foundation for the Accreditation of Hematopoietic Cell Therapy (FAHCT) in mid-summer 2001 and currently is the only FAHCT-accredited program in the Carolinas.

In its first decade, WFUBMC's program performed over 950 bone marrow transplants on adults and older young people—more than any adult transplant program in the state.

Transplantation has become the treatment of choice for a number of cancers, Pennell said, and the Medical Center is currently participating in transplantation clinical trials with the National Heart, Lung, and Blood Institute (NHLBI), Cancer and Leukemia Group B (CALGB), and research in the transplantation field.

Here at the turn of the century, the cancer center is spreading its arm of specialized knowledge and care into chosen areas of cancer research, specifically—but not exclusively—the brain, breast, blood cells, colon, lung, and prostate, all prevalent in the South and the state. Through multidisciplinary programs, Pennell said, patients are getting the most effective and timely treatment made in consultation with specialists in radiation, medical, surgical, and pathology oncology. Working together, these specialists are making significant progress in early detection and the latest treatment options.

The first goal of the center's Cancer Control Program (CCP), Pennell said, is prevention and detection, reliable keys for halting new cases. With NCI-funded research, CCP conducts its clinical intervention studies locally and regionally, particularly among African Americans, Native Americans, the elderly, and those with low incomes or those living in rural areas.

More often the studies are focused on those cancers prevalent among women. Women getting regular screenings for breast, cervical, and colorectal cancers have reduced incidents, morbidity, and mortality from cancer. The program, Pennell explained, further increases these chances of survival by offering classes on nutrition, behavioral attitudes, breast and skin self-examinations, and awareness of inherited tendencies as well as treatment availabilities.

CCP cancer-awareness programs across the state have alerted women and primary care physicians of increased clinical trial opportunities, screening inclusiveness, and community-based intervention education offered by the Medical Center program.

Pennell noted that breast cancer deaths have been slowing for white and Hispanic women and for the first time for young black women but not for older black women.

Death rates from prostate cancer have decreased sharply for white men and increased for black men but not for Hispanic males. Both new cases and deaths from cancer of the colon and rectum have declined for both sexes, due in part to physicians' and spouses' pleas for regular screenings and in part to America's reluctant gravity toward a less fat diet with increased daily servings of vegetables and fruit and to a less sedentary lifestyle.

The American Cancer Society (ACS) has given the medical school a $1 million five-year study grant, Pennell said, to look for more effective intervention strategies among low-income minority women over age 50.

This partnership study, begun in 2000 between the medical school and the Southeast Division of the ACS, is an effort to improve colorectal cancer screening among African-American women whose survival rate from it is lower.

WFUBMC's Breast Cancer Center of Excellence, funded by a NCI grant, was developed in 1996, Pennell said, in order to unify all their scientific studies in this area and to reduce duplication of efforts. By pulling together all their findings, he added, researchers can intermesh all their pioneering knowledge on this common form of carcinoma and better strive in unison toward total eradication of abnormal cells which form a mass or tumor that may be either benign or malignant. Malignant cells can invade a primary site and then use the bloodstream or lymphatic system to travel to other parts of the body to form new tumors.

Meanwhile, researchers and physicians continue to apply their comprehensive treatment protocols and clinical studies and review their applications and outcomes. When evidence supports a tried-and-true technique, it can be applied safely as a proven cancer therapy approved by CPS, Pennell said.

Today, he explained, there is no one cause for breast cancer, the most common form of carcinoma among women. It is believed to be a combination of genetics and lifestyle. There is no one way known to catch its onset except through early detection by frequent routine examinations by patients and physicians and regular mammograms. A better lifestyle can improve health in general, but it does not protect women from breast cancer, which has its individualized way of developing within the body.

Breast cancer, the second-leading cause of death among women, Pennell explained, does not discriminate among its victims, either by age, sex, race, or geographical location, but its prejudice is focused about 95 percent on women and only about 1 to 5 percent on men.

It is reported, Pennell said, "that breast cancer is back on the increase. One out of every eight women in America today, living to be 80, will get breast cancer." The increase may be due to increased self-examinations, improved mammographic techniques, and advanced screening technologies that allow very slow-growing cancers to be detected before they are symptomatic, especially among older women.

Thus, Pennell added, periodical screenings are advised as part of women's ongoing health care. Ordering screenings does not mean physicians think cancer is present, he explained. This is solely a precautionary step, for screenings are done when there are no symptoms. When physicians suspect cancer, they order diagnostic tests.

"The best method for treating breast cancer," Pennell said, is debatable among physicians, "but surgery still remains the prime defense. We are still struggling on the best way to manage that. I think the results between lumpectomy—removing only the tumor followed by radiation, which allows breast preservation—as opposed to total mastectomy or total breast removal and lymph node dissection or sampling with either procedure are equal. That is, the results are equal in selected tumors. The advantage of a lumpectomy, combined with radiation and lymph node removal, is that the lady gets to keep her breast. The disadvantage is that she is going to receive radiation treatment five days a week for six weeks. Although greatly decreased, some side effects of radiation are still a risk.

"When there are multiple tumors or they are too large for a lumpectomy, a mastectomy with lymph node removal is recommended. Even with some of the mildest forms of breast cancers, a mastectomy is often needed. Some have likened this to taking a sledgehammer to kill a gnat.

"Obviously the disadvantage of a mastectomy is that the lady loses her breast, but she can immediately get on with life without radiation. Reconstruction of the breast can take place immediately or later and that results in a breast mound, not a breast. Furthermore, there are some tumors, because of size and location, such as under the nipple, that make it difficult or unwise to do a lumpectomy.

"To be able to do a lumpectomy successfully," Pennell added, "one of the key criteria is to obtain adequate margins or edges where there are no tumor cells. Getting those margins sometimes is difficult, and, for that reason, a lumpectomy sometimes can be disfiguring. Or the tumor may be so multicentric or diffused that one has to go back and do a mastectomy.

"Some of the milder, less-aggressive cancers of the breast, called DCIS (ductal carcinoma *in situ*), show no microscopic evidence of invasion and may be too small to feel. They are not the most difficult to treat, but there is more controversy about the management of these lesions. Their detection unequivocally has increased because of better mammogram techniques."

One of the greatest strides that has been made with regard to cancer, Pennell said, "is improved care, both with surgery and with treatment, involving radiation, chemotherapy, and hormone-blocking drugs." Radiation energy, he explained, kills cancer cells at the site of the tumor removal, including the surrounding area and nearby lymph nodes. Chemotherapy chemicals kill rapidly multiplying cancer cells. Hormone-blocking drugs, such as tamoxifen, interfere with the actions of hormones supporting cancer cell growth.

Often a combination of these treatment plans is used, Pennell noted, because much about breast cancer treatment still remains unknown. Treatment, he added, "is begun soon after surgery in order to halt the cancer and to promote extended survival, depending, of course, upon the stage and age of the patient and the aggressiveness of the tumor.

"The bottom line on what procedure to do in breast cancer—and I think this is most important—rests with the patient herself and what she wants, how much her breast means to her and her own self-image, lovemaking, and other personal factors.

"And I think any well-informed, well-educated woman can make that decision for herself, and that is how I have always tried to work it. I give the patient and spouse the opportunity to make a choice with the advice and in consultation with radiation oncologists, myself, and, when needed, medical oncologists. If reconstruction is to be considered, a plastic surgeon becomes involved.

"Now are both radiation and chemotherapy needed? It depends upon whether the lymph nodes are involved and whether the markers are aggressive. If it is a very fierce tumor, especially in young women even with no node involvement, we usually advise chemotherapy. It improves the cure and disease-free intervals."

In women over 70, Pennell said, "a somewhat different set of rules and criteria apply, at present, depending upon the type of tumor. All that may be necessary is a lumpectomy. Lymph node removal usually is not done unless they are palpable or it is a highly aggressive tumor. Most of us feel node removal does not add to cure but helps stage the disease. If, however, it is a large tumor or multicentric, a simple mastectomy may be needed.

"Most of these tumors in older women," Pennell added, "are detected by mammography. There are those cancer specialists and statisticians who feel many of these women would have died of some other cause before the cancer became 'active.'

"Some individuals feel that the marked increase in incidents of cancer of the breast in our country is a result of better mammographic detection of this group of tumors."

And that detection will be helped further, Pennell explained, by a new imaging technology developed by a medical school professor whose technology is called Tuned-Aperture Computed Tomography (TACT). The device allows radiologists to see objects, such as tumors, within the dense part of the breasts, regions that often before were obscured by overlying tissues. The FDA has approved TACT.

Another recent discovery made by medical school oncologists, Pennell said, is heated chemotherapy used in conjunction with surgery as a method of treating certain types of advanced abdominal and ovarian cancers. The process has extended the lives of patients who had no further treatment options. It also is being used in clinical trials for the treatment of gastrointestinal tumors and other tumors that have spread into the lining of the abdomen. It has been found that heating increases the effectiveness of the cancer drug's interaction.

Colorectal cancer—like breast cancer—needs the clues of early recognition, Pennell said, particularly if genetic mapping shows there is a family history of the disease. High-risk people, or those predisposed to this cancer of the large intestines and rectum, need to be aware that they might genetically inherit it.

These patients, he advised, "need to be observant of stool changes, such as discoloration, either dark melena or bright blood, increased mucus, and decreased size or shape of stool, and report them to their physicians.

"Early stages of colon cancers can be identified," Pennell reported, "if patients undergo regular screenings and take periodical detection tests, looking for polyps or other premalignant conditions. Here again, once patients' DNA printouts are available, physicians will have clues as to the probability of inherited cells' destiny to become faulty and likely to mutate and multiply."

Melanoma, the most lethal of skin cancers, he said, is on the rise, after a plateau, as Americans neglect to use sunscreens or to get professional skin examinations. The only hope to cure this aggressive cancer is early detection and early surgical intervention before its cells dig deeper and spread. Melanoma does not respond well either to chemical or radiation therapy or to any treatment other than surgical removal, but Pennell believes genetic decoding will help in finding its cure.

Wake Forest's cancer detectors have found that the minimal invasion implantation of radioactive iodine "seeds" to treat prostate cancer returns most men to normalcy within a year.

This program, called brachytherapy, is one of three treatment options for early-stage prostate cancer, Pennell said. The others are the removal of the prostate—classed as the most successful—or standard radiation dosages, both of which may include the side effects of impotence and incontinence.

Here again early discovery is paramount, Pennell explained, otherwise, this cancer can leave its home base in the prostate and run a wild course within the body. At advanced stages or with exceedingly aggressive tumors, conventional treatment options may strike out, leaving patients in agony and with lessened prospects for a prolonged life.

The Prostate Cancer Center of Excellence at WFUBMC was founded in 1999 through a $5 million grant from Baptist Hospital. The center focuses on improving treatment outcomes for more than 10,000 men in North Carolina who will be diagnosed each year with the disease.

Medical Center investigators hope to determine if patients' own bodies can trigger immune cells to halt the multiplying of prostate cancer cells and if patients' blood can be fed antigens that send out "killer" cells on search-and-destroy missions against "sick" cells. Team members believe this multidepartmental study ultimately will reduce the mortality and morbidity of prostate cancer victims.

In the summer of 2001, the Medical Center began participating in the largest-ever prostate cancer prevention trial, sponsored by NCI and the Southwest Oncology Group. The 12-year study will follow men age 55 and over who are in generally good health to determine if two dietary supplements, selenium and vitamin E, either separately or together, can protect them against this second most common form of cancer. A total of 32,400 men who have never had prostate cancer are being recruited from 400 sites in the United States, Puerto Rico, and Canada to participate in the Selenium and Vitamin E Cancer Prevention Trial (SELECT).

Since African-American men have the highest incidence of prostate cancer in the world and at a younger age, they may enroll at age 50. There is no upper age limit.

Selenium and vitamin E, both naturally occurring nutrients, are antioxidants capable of neutralizing toxins or free radicals that might possibly lead to cancer.

In a 1996 study of selenium to prevent non-melanoma skin cancer, researchers found that it did not reduce skin cancer but did decrease the incidence of prostate cancer in men by more than 60 percent.

In a 1998 trial studying the possibility of beta-carotene and vitamin E preventing lung cancer, it was learned that 32 percent of the men taking the vitamin had less prostate cancer but neither the vitamin or the compound found in dark green and dark yellow vegetables and fruits prevented lung cancer.

NIH has awarded the cancer center a grant in complementary and alternative medicine to study the prevention and treatment of prostate cancer using other natural products, such as bee pollen, fish oils containing vitamin D, and lycopene, an extract found in tomatoes.

This research grant illustrates renewed belief in the power of natural compounds to heal, promote health, and fight disease, something medical practitioners have been interested in for centuries.

Prostate cancer is the most common form of cancer affecting men in America, followed by lung cancer, the nation's leading cause of cancer deaths.

The best way to interrupt lung cancer's presence—or spread—within the body, Pennell explained, is a two-step approach: find it early and treat it early.

For those wanting to quit smoking, thought to be the common cause of lung cancer, help is found in patches, gums, drugs, and changes in behavioral patterns, such as less stress. All are designed to help kick the tobacco habit or to go the cold turkey route.

The use of spiral CT scanning to screen for lung cancer is the latest tool for the earliest intervention and is available at the Medical Center along with routine chest X-rays and conventional CAT scans.

As with all cancer patients, he continued, the Medical Center's umbrella of care goes beyond medical breakthroughs to the physiology of rehabilitation, counseling, exercise nutrition, and ongoing health maintenance.

Its 20-year-old Cancer Patient Support Program (CPSP), a national model for holistic health care, helps patients meet the emotional and psychological challenges of cancer, Pennell said. Center caretakers teach their patients the life-protecting skills of coping with the after-shocks of cancer discovery and treatment recovery. Among them is the value of exercise during chemotherapy and radiation to combat fatigue and boost well-being.

The primary goal in all cancer treatment is not only to suppress its development but also its spread, Pennell said. Those within the Medical Center's research arm are seeking answers from clinical trials or research studies on human subjects, he added. They are asking, "How well are new experimental drugs working on cancer?" and "How safe are they in comparison to current and proven in-use therapies?"

In its overseeing role, CPS questions all clinical trials and evaluates answers from its scientists and physicians as to whether the research benefits patients with cancer or heart diseases or any other disorders.

As Medical Center researchers integrate both departmental and multidisciplinary findings, Pennell said, they enhance patient care. Patients not only will be the recipients of new discoveries for their heart and cancer problems, for example, but they may even participate in clinical trials that will help lead to new treatments.

Medical Center researchers know, Pennell said, that healthy habits effectively extend and benefit lives, especially those with or predisposed to heart and stroke problems, an area they began investigating 40 years ago with arteriosclerosis research that soon moved to multidisciplinary efforts to benefit victims of cancer and stroke.

They acknowledge that lifestyle changes are difficult, but their benefits are dramatic and their outcomes mean lower risk of hearth disease, lower cholesterol and blood pressure levels, and reduced overall risks of death from all causes.

To feel better, live better, and live longer, Pennell explained, patients do have a choice: to be in the low- or high-risk category of health. Lower means reduced fat intake, increased exercise, balanced meals, and avoidance of smoking and excess alcohol and weight. Higher can be equated to self-inflicted disabilities.

Only 10 percent of Americans are at a low risk for heart attack, have a cholesterol level of less than 200, and a blood pressure reading of 120/80 or lower, Pennell reported. This means that the greater majority of Americans has ignored prevention despite its proven reward.

That leaves intervention, Pennell said, and the Medical Center has that capability.

Statistics show that African-American men are more likely to die from heart disease than American Indian, Hispanic, and white men, especially those in the rural South, so Medical Center heart care providers stress prevention intervention.

WFUBMC's Heart Center surgeons have performed cardiac surgery since the World War II era, have pioneered open-heart surgery in North Carolina for nearly a half-century, and made major contributions in interventional cardiology services. For a half-century Wake Forest's scientists have studied arteriosclerosis, the root cause of most heart attacks and strokes. It remains a major research effort by them because of the propensity of Southerners to fall victims to these two major bodily debilitators. And over the years, these scientists have contributed much to what is known about diet and arteriosclerosis through research on animal models.

As the Heart Center grew and expanded, Pennell said, so did its services, all under the close scrutiny of CPS. Today it offers the best therapeutic options available, including angioplasty that reopens diseased blood vessels, atherectomy that clears plaque from cholesterol and fatty build-up, stents that hold open coronary arteries to improve blood flow into heart muscles, and statins that lower cholesterol. And it still relies on one of the oldest over-the-counter drugs, aspirin, to thin the blood.

In the past, for nearly two decades, cardiologists with open arms have welcomed scientific breakthroughs in heart-care advancements, for diseases of the heart attack both men and women of all ages. More women have died of cardiovascular diseases in the past two decades, Pennell said, but more men undergo angioplasty and bypass surgery and three-fourths of heart transplant surgery is performed on males.

Today, Pennell added, the leading cause of death for women is heart attacks and strokes, nearly twice that of cancer deaths and about 10 times that of breast cancer. While physicians cannot change women's genetic composition, women can adopt lifestyle changes that stave off cardiovascular diseases. Pennell said the recipe is to start early in adulthood to stop smoking, eat correctly, manage weight, get exercise, and take drugs to hold down blood pressure and cholesterol levels.

Pennell said the Heart Center routinely does coronary artery bypass surgery to increase blood and oxygen supply to the heart, valve replacement and repair, pulmonary resections, great vessel surgery on adults and children, and increasingly neonatal surgery to correct congenital heart problems. A multidisciplinary cardiac team identifies the needs of patients, evaluates their health status, and recommends a plan of action to be implemented.

Most patients with heart failure, he explained, can be stabilized. When this is not possible, cardiac transplantation, begun in 1985, is an option. "Because of its outstanding results in heart and lung transplants," Pennell said, "this Heart Center's capabilities are probably the best on the eastern seaboard. The complex aortic valve replacement or repair is another exceptional procedure performed at the Medical Center. It allows the heart to pump blood to meet the needs of the body's tissues."

WFUBMC researchers took part in a national 10-year study of cardiovascular disease risk in the elderly sponsored by the National Heart, Lung, and Blood Institute.

Its findings, released in February 2001, are of primary importance in the treatment of the disease. The study showed, Pennell said, that 55 percent of its congestive heart failure participants did not have the type of heart failure usually associated with this serious condition—a weakened heart muscle unable to pump enough blood to meet the body's requirements for oxygen and nutrients, thus causing systolic heart failure. Rather, the participants had a second form or diastolic failure, which may be more prevalent among the elderly, especially women who had 67 percent diastolic failure as compared to 42 percent among men.

This newer form of heart failure, researchers learned, is not fully understood as to cause, progression, or treatment. The implications of the study are enormous in that heart failure, the number one cause of hospitalization for people age 65 and older, is classified as one of the largest health problems in the developed world.

Heart failure does not mean that the heart has stopped, Pennell explained. Rather, it means the heart is not able to keep up with its duties. Heart failure has many causes and no known cure exists, but basic treatment approaches give patients extended life. This means reducing sodium intake, taking antibiotics if heart infection exists and diuretics if there is fluid retention, no smoking or drinking alcohol, eating appropriately, following a moderate exercise plan, and taking drugs, if needed, for high blood pressure and an overactive thyroid.

The standard treatment for systolic heart failure, Pennell said, includes taking water pills, blood thinners, and medications that cause blood vessels to widen or increase the force of heart contractions.

The Heart Center, he explained, has its own repository of cardiac prevention tools, ranging from cardiac catheterization, a test that provides information about the pumping ability of the heart muscle; to coronary angiography, an X-ray examination of the precise size of blood vessels or chambers of the heart; to angioplasty procedures that clear clogged artery blockages depriving the heart of oxygen. With the aid of various discovery machines, cardiac surgeons diagnose intervention possibilities. The echocardiography, called ECG or EKG, measures the heart's electrical impulses to determine if the heart has been damaged. An MRI creates a computer-generated picture of the cardiac chambers and large vessels, which helps diagnose and evaluate certain types of cardiac diseases. Positron emission tomography (PET) is another non-invasive study that yields information about heart tissue function used for treatment strategies. PET is also a major player in cancer diagnostics. Transesophageal echocardiography (TEE) is an ultrasound test used for producing a moving image of the heart during cardiac valve or high-risk artery surgery.

The Medical Center is continuing its research into hypertension or high blood pressure and how drugs regulate blood pressure. The five-year study began in 1999, made possible by a $7.5 million NIH grant. It is based on a discovery the Wake Forest research team made in 1989: the identification of a new hormone that helps regulate blood pressure.

Hypertension is a major risk factor for cardiovascular disease, the leading killer of both men and women in America. Fewer than 23 percent of adults have blood pressure in the optimum range. The Southeast has the highest rate of strokes in the nation. And that is why the Medical Center has a Comprehensive Stroke Care unit, which is constantly investigating new ways to dissolve clots that cause strokes.

The medical school is using its $450,000 grant from the National Heart, Lung, and Blood Institute for a community-based educational-project designed to reduce the incidence of strokes among African Americans living in Davie, Forsyth, Stokes, Surry, and Yadkin counties. The premise of the Stroke Education and Awareness Among Minorities Project is to mobilize African-American community and church advocates and health professionals to promote cardiovascular disease prevention through screenings that check blood pressure, cholesterol, triglycerides, body fat, and glucose. WFUSM is one of 12 centers in the nation focusing on the high-risk by minorities to die from heart disease and stroke, especially in the Southeast and particularly in the Piedmont.

Just as this project seeks to monitor and eliminate disparities among races for equal health care, so does CPS, as it seeks ways to turn-around *all* patients' lives from seasons of hopelessness to hopefulness.

XIII   THE MEDICINE OF MORTALITY

After the medicine of immortality no longer can hold onto life, physicians must offer the medicine of mortality.

Humans, at birth, pass through the gates of life. Medicine now can help them bypass the gates of hell. For today, physicians have the desire and wont to alleviate painful deaths with human kindness.

Just as they practiced good-life measures, physicians now are practicing good-death options, teaching themselves, patients, spouses, families, and friends the art of release—relinquishing the body going silent.

"Good death," Pennell said, is not a prescription for doctor-assisted suicide or euthanasia but rather a prescription for end-of-life support and compassion that says: "We are here for you." "We will not abandon you." "We can deflect your pain." "We will not compromise your care." "We will support your stated wishes."

This means, he added, that as physicians practice the humanizing of life, so, too, can they practice the humanizing of death.

Doctors who have gone through the training and practice of health care are acquainted with life and death, but those experiences do not make them any better prepared than others in accepting the inevitability of the death watch.

Physicians' hardest melancholy ministry still is letting go, releasing bodies from machine-only living, and stopping the process of lifesaving medicine. For them it is acceptance of defeat—as it is for those dying. But physicians are confronted with this season of health care because 80 percent of Americans now die either in hospitals or nursing-care facilities.

To keep patients alive through technology, when the seeds of death are evident, has become a terminal practice that benefits neither the dying nor the living. Final illnesses today often become the patients' most costly.

In this awesome age of medicine, there is no magical pill that promises nonending life. So, recognizing this reality, the Medical Center has in place rules of guidance that assist patients and physicians in their final relationships—for no one is fully alert to the exact hour of death's blow.

In February 2000, CPS approved updated procedures regarding patients' rights to a natural death and withholding or withdrawing therapy policies. These, originally prepared by the Medical Center's Ethics Committee, became effective in 1990 and were reviewed in 1999.

They include the right to accept or refuse medical, mental health, or surgical treatment, and the right to formulate advance directives, such as living wills or health care powers of attorney, and advance instructions for mental health treatment. These decision-making issues are more common in today's medical care. Their inclusion in the health history-taking procedure gives both patients and physicians in-place guidelines.

These policies, Pennell explained, cover therapies that are provided for patients who are not suffering from cardiopulmonary arrest and who do not require resuscitative therapies. The withholding and withdrawal policies, he added, cover nonresuscitative therapy decisions that are in accordance with natural death wishes.

"These policies," he said, "recognize that provisions of medical therapy should always be decided on the basis of the benefits to patients and the standards of medical practice rather than family needs or interests."

He defined withholding as not providing or initiating heroic therapy, whereas withdrawing means stopping or discontinuing heroic therapies. Under this hospital policy, he said, "there is no moral difference from withholding therapy determined to be extraordinary and withdrawing therapy determined to be extraordinary or futile."

Primarily, he continued, it is the responsibility of attending physicians in consultation with patients—where possible or from written instructions—to make the decisions regarding withholding or withdrawing. If patients' requests are unknown and documents are not available or do not exist, then decisions are left to the discretion of the attending physicians.

If patients are incompetent, incurable, or in vegetative states, or have no directives, Pennell said, attending physicians get permission either from patients' guardians, spouses, parents (if patients are minors), or the majority decision of relatives of the first order. In more complicated situations, he said, permission rules become more complicated.

JCAHO, he added, requires that Baptist Hospital document patients' self-determination intents whether they are or are not available.

The State of North Carolina, Pennell said, has three advance directive statutes: declaration of a desire for a natural death or a living will, health care power of attorney, and procedures for natural death or the absence of a declaration, all recognized by CPS.

Cardiopulmonary resuscitation is performed on all patients at Baptist who suffer cardiac or respiratory arrest unless specific orders to the contrary are written, Pennell explained. The presence of a DNR order does not imply total withdrawal of usual and customary care of patients.

When cure is no longer an option, Pennell said, palliative care is invoked. Its emphasis is on easing pain and misery when the physical body is going silent and on providing comfort and presence for the dying, letting them die with the same degree of dignity with which they lived.

Pennell believes the patient self-determination policies reflect the Medical Center's values of compassion and integrity that ensure that all aspects of patient care are provided by the institution in a caring and humane manner. The hospital and its medical staff by accepting and abiding by these policies said they would still continue their commitment to uphold the preservation of life, the alleviation of suffering, and the promotion of the health of their patients—within the organization's capacity and within applicable laws and regulations.

Mortal sleep, Pennell said, comes to all people. It is not something that people want to think about, he added, but eventually they should.

"One learns there are those ultimate deaths that are merciful, appropriate, and releasing. But there are other deaths that are extremely difficult to accept. Every patient is a friend. Every patient is an ally. You are their advocate. It is never easy.

"There are a large number of patients who do not want to talk specifically about death because they have a pathological fear of it. And if they do, you must address this before you can help them.

"I do think that for those individuals who have a *healthy*, meaningful relationship with God—through an understanding of His promises of the life hereafter—that death is easier. It is less final. But here I must emphasize the word *healthy*.

"The individual who is under conviction that the disease or illness was inflicted by God because of his or her sin is a very hard person to deal with. It is even more difficult for medical professionals to help these individuals who are convinced that God will cure them or that God is 'calling them home.' Often neither wants us to interfere nor practice medicine in their behalf.

"I have great difficulty forcing anybody to do anything.

"There are many ramifications that make death and dying and even health and treatment difficult to deal with. There are choices: dying sooner or living slightly longer. The choices of the family may not be that of the patient who has accepted that there is no hope for cure.

"One never knows the day or hour of death, but you must help the patient and the family come to terms with the inevitable."

It is essential, Pennell said, for the physician to know what it is like to be the patient and how to handle failure of health. "I have been a patient and like my patients I have been at the mercy of my physician. Whenever I wondered how to handle telling the patient bad news, I asked myself, 'How would I have wanted this handled?' 'How would I want to be told?' 'How much would I want to be told?' I go back to the Golden Rule concept. If providers and physicians don't reflect on that every day, they are going to shortchange the recipients in their care.

"I believe I am prepared for death through the doctrine of grace, so in all honesty I do not spend a whole lot of time thinking about it."

Medical advancements are accelerating at unbelievable speed, Pennell said, and this means "that the average patient is living longer. For those who are healthy at age 80 and can play golf, fish, read, eat, exercise, or do whatever they want, life is great. But for the decrepit 80-year-old, it may not be good. The issue then becomes, 'What is quality of life?' Each individual must define that."

The goal of skillful medical practitioners is to save and redeem lives and deter death, he explained, but all the cures and controls cannot bypass life's invisible shadow.

"Where there is hope," he added, "I reassure my patients. When there is no hope, I cannot lie. I cannot say, 'Don't worry. We're going to find a miracle treatment or cure within the next six months.' You cannot do that."

When medicine cannot cure and lives cannot be recaptured, Pennell said, a physician's last duty "is to maintain the dignity of patients. Aside from trauma, virtually all deaths are quiet. There is little thrashing and that kind of thing."

Pennell drew on his love of nature to explain what he meant.

"When an eagle swoops down to catch a fish or rabbit or squirrel, it is known that some type of substance is released in the body of the captured. For the lack of a better term, it has been called 'relaxin.' I think that many people on their way to emerging death experience that 'relaxin,' and that is the reason they are not fighting, struggling for life. I think there is a point when people give up. They just quit fighting. Part of this is depression and part of it is realism, or maybe it is the beginning of that 'relaxin' stage.

"The person quits breathing when the heart stops pumping blood. Most deaths are anticipated. If it is an expected death, we try to move the patient into a private room so that he or she can have some quiet and privacy with family and friends.

"The greatest majority of people usually know that they are going to die. They will ask you that. They want to know more about what's going on. Some are afraid. Others aren't.

"One of the ethical and religious questions often asked is: 'Do Christians die more peacefully?' There are those who argue they do, and there are those who say they cannot see any difference. Still others say the question is rationalization."

There are those who undergo the classic die-and-come-back experience. "I don't know if they catch glimpses of 'another world,' but invariably the ones I've talked to describe bright lights and a pleasantness, a peace."

When Pennell encountered near-death during surgery and saved a patient's life, he was "grateful to God for the opportunity and to those who taught me and provided me with the knowledge and experience.

"Death taught me how important it is to be sensitive to patients' individual needs and to respect both life and death. Their families taught me what a good healthy relationship can and should be like and what a guilt-ridden relationship is like.

"I think it is tragic when a patient's terminal weeks and months are filled with pain. You do whatever can be done to control it. Pain is a strange thing: It affects people differently. The same stimulant that produces pain in one patient may be excruciating to one person and minimal in another. Just as reaction to pain is different, so are the pain-relief medications. Here again each person is unique. You have to individualize the treatment for each person.

"No physician, including those in oncology and neurology where there is a high loss rate, ever gets acclimated to losing patients. We struggle with loss. There are many deaths, particularly the unexpected—and they do occur—when we truly agonize over them."

Today physicians and caregivers try never to let the terminally ill lapse into agony or neglect just because their health has been identified as "unredeemable," Pennell explained.

And that, he said, is the importance of the sustaining gift of palliative and hospice care.

At death, as in life, Pennell applies his rule for honesty and compassion: "I assure the family that we did everything possible. I give them the freedom to respond. Sometimes they take their hostilities out on me, or the system, or life in general. They are angry and frustrated and they feel the need to take out their sadness on somebody. Sometimes you just have to stand in and play that role for a period of time. They forget that we, too, are sad, but, as the physician, we do not have that privilege at that time."

Early in the 20th century, the physician was the friend-doctor who tended the patient and family. Death did not diminish that relationship. Just as the patient and physician broached death before its arrival, physician and family expressed their grief together after death. This one-on-one conversation helped them to intimately confront their wound. Both were relieved they could express their genuine loss to one another. The physician could confess once again that there was nothing else he could have done; the family was grateful for his loyalty and honesty.

But today the end-watch often can be different, for when death's knock is heard, far-flung family members may not respond and some practitioners may appear to have abandoned the case. The physician at that moment, however, may not be able to make closure with patient or family, for he or she may be involved in making crucial emergency decisions or procedures on other patients.

At the Medical Center, medical students have the option to sign up for studies that teach them the medical art of death compassion. The School of Pastoral Care teaches ministers—clergy and laity—and spiritual leaders in churches, businesses, and counselors the spiritual art of treating both body and soul.

While other medical centers are exploring the connection between medicine and faith, WFUBMC was founded on this belief.

Medical practitioners here recognize that patients' belief systems can be doubly used for healing and coping with life's end.

It is not unusual on the hospital's halls to hear and see caregivers tend their patients with a spiritual reverence. They acknowledge that it is a place where they can practice the same value system they observe at home and in church. Demonstrated compassion often allows patients to feel they are in a safe haven. This stance can be harder in this century because work demands can be so consuming that personal time with patients is lessened, but well-meaning caretakers have compassionate ways to sustain the well-being of their patients while tending to medical machines that require user-friendly attitudes.

These medical life-extenders marvel when the art and science of healing push death further back into the shadows—and they are there to help this possibility.

This extended-life period, Pennell said, "can give patients time to make peace with family and friends—and the inevitable."

For care supporters, this is a time to accept and dignify the road life travels toward death and journey's end.

XIV A MISSION THAT GREW OFF THE HILL

The Medical Center's foundation is set into steel embedded deep into Hawthorne Hill, known for its massive stone understructure that ensures rock-solid stability for the buildings huddling across the hillside.

Before the steel came gifts of stability from benefactors who wished to make total medical care a mission possibility in Piedmont North Carolina and across the state.

Within the first decade after the hospital and medical school joined, the Medical Center became a benefactor of its own by enlarging its goodwill and mission beyond Northwest North Carolina.

What began may be one of the Medical Center's most untold achievements: corporate and personal involvement in health care delivery around the world.

When Pennell entered medical school, faculty members already were engaged in "foreign-soil" medicine. They were helping other nations establish their own medical schools, training doctors and nurses beyond the rudiments for medical missionary work, accepting Nationals into medical programs for study here, receiving internationals as visiting scholars, sending volunteer teams to hospital ships and missions or bush clinics operated by a variety of faiths other than Southern Baptists.

Pennell aspired to add to these statistics by being one who trained at home and served abroad. Doors opened in other directions, so he did not enter the field full time, but he never lost the interest, the summons, or the chance to serve as an active on-call medical missionary volunteer, consultant, and evaluator.

"My involvement in missions," he explained, "was an integral, ongoing, important, and central portion of my life, dating way back before medical school. I felt totally unqualified and unequivocally unfit, but Christ looks for all kinds of people. He shows you your possibilities.

"I did not change so much in call as direction of call. I began to realize that my contributions to medical missions could be as great—if not greater—as what I was doing here. I was able to provide a liaison between medical missions and hospitals around the world. With the Medical Center, I was able to help medical students maintain their covenant, commitment, and opportunity for medical missionary service. And, I hope, I helped take continuing medical education for missionary and National physicians working in mission hospitals to a much higher level.

"I think countless people involved in missions—not just medical missions—found they had a friend here who understood and supported them, so unequivocally this was one of the most rewarding components of my life: personally, professionally, intellectually, spiritually, in every way. "

Since the 1960s, he has Pied-Pipered others to find their way into mission work. In so doing, he used his invaluable contacts and knowledge to enlarge even more widely the Medical Center's contributions to worldwide medicine, whether the involvement was secular, religious, academic, clinical, or political.

In 1982, the medical school, under Janeway's leadership, established the Office of International Health Affairs to expand the school's presence in worldwide health and medicine, a decision recognized by the Association of American Medical Colleges. Pennell became its first director, a logical decision since he was, by far, one of the faculty most closely associated with and personally involved in international community health and development.

It is apparent, Pennell said, looking at the emergence of Asia, that part of the great economic future of the world and the United States eventually will be tied to whatever happens to the Pacific Rim, and the Medical Center wanted a presence there.

Currently, he added, formal affiliations are established with medical schools in China, India, Japan, Italy, Norway, South America, and other health care facilities around the world. True affiliates, he added, are not just recipients of expert American medical advisors. "They must have something they can contribute to us—to save face and to save pride. We want our affiliates to be able to stand on their own."

International Health Fellows from around the globe, he explained, come to the medical school for advanced training. The concept of this program is one of return: What they learn here, they take back to the countries of their origin to apply there.

Senior medical students and residents take advantage of overseas electives, both in nonindustrialized and industrialized countries, to better understand the problems and contributions that can be made and to earn credits in community health.

Each year about 40 medical school faculty members serve as advisors to students interested in overseas projects. Each year over 100 faculty members actively participate in continuing foreign-held medical education conferences or are involved with their on-site deliberations at foreign locations. And many others share their expertise through ham radio consultations to those with emergency medical problems.

Because of International Health's leadership, medical school graduates and alumni satisfy their itch to serve in both full- and part-time mission assignments.

The vastness of these arms of exchange continues to grow as they do with visiting scholars and administrators who, once they return home, are referring their patients in critical situations to the Medical Center where they witnessed firsthand its excellence in diagnostic and specialty medicine and care.

In any given year, Baptist Hospital provides approximately $250,000 through its International Benevolent Care Fund to care for needy foreign patients who come to it in hopes of miracles known only to modern science. The hospital has become a beacon of hope for these people with seemingly hopeless maladies, Pennell said. Both the hospital and physicians working with the needy "waive their fees, and I think this is appropriate," Pennell said, "for this gratitude is evidence of their belief that neither patients nor medicine should know any boundaries when it comes to health care."

A second—and separate—international health service program was spawned in 1998. Its concept is to attract affluent patients who want to come to this country for their health care delivery. Many of these patients, Pennell said, "have been going to places like the Mayo Clinic or Cleveland Clinic. They are willing to pay upfront for the Medical Center's outstanding service and treatment. Many come here for reconstructive or plastic surgery as well as cardiac and orthopaedic services."

Benevolent care patients continue to come through the Office of International Health—those referred but without insurance or ability to pay, the program Pennell directed.

The leadership of Wake Forest University and the hospital, Pennell explained, supports this wing of medicine. This global vision is based on their commitment to heal the sick regardless of human illness or language spoken.

"Believe it or not," Pennell said, "medicine is a formidable, international, political, and diplomatic tool. The goodwill alone contributed by American medicine is truly significant. For those of us in academics and in clinical settings, we must continue to provide individualized training for the expatriate physicians. This is especially true for those who return to their own countries. This is one way we can and should be involved. There is no doubt—absolutely no doubt—that North American medicine, specifically that of the United States, is now the most recognized and respected health care delivery in the world. That is especially true in clinical care and training."

The Medical Center has learned, Pennell said, that hands-on involvement in international health is not a one-time learning experience. "It is the fastest way to grasp fully the magnitude of worldwide need for improved and expanded health care delivery. The needs of people, patients, and consumers are not the only ones we immediately encounter. I am convinced—and studies document this—that the most lasting benefits and most significant rewards derived from this type of involvement are first to the individuals who provide it and second to the physicians and caregivers with whom these volunteers work. Such tours invariably result in long-term relationships—not only friendships but continuing assistance through medical help, supplies, and support.

"Short-term volunteers," he continued, "usually contribute in three important ways: letting the struggling physician in a very difficult, deprived situation know that someone cares, appreciates them, and is willing to help; providing these individuals with intense, continuing medical education training, updating medical procedures, and professional fellowship; and providing these individuals with an ongoing connection with the best health care delivery system in the world. Involvement of this type changes perspectives and insights—even awareness—and improves concepts of international politics and relationships so much so that the number of people returning for more short-term involvement exceeds 75 percent."

Health care delivery in most of the Third World countries is often at least 20 years behind current medical practices, Pennell said. "Those of us who have seen and know tuberculosis, chronic osteos, massive hernias, extensive tumors, thyroids, and uteri and ovarian cysts, or who can recall less sophisticated, technological days when our physical diagnostic capabilities and expertise were more important than the current defensive medicine can make formidable contributions. Those trained only in a technologically oriented world can learn tremendously from this experience, especially now that 'old' diseases are resurfacing.

"There are many personal gratifications to be gained from this involvement, tangible and intangible. Expressions of appreciation for medical personnel are loud and clear—something increasingly difficult to hear, see, or experience in this country.

"Although we speak a different language, follow a different philosophy, and have different objectives than most of the world, we can and should build bridges of peace, understanding, and friendship. We in medicine must not lose sight of this or lose control of our capability to help.

"Working with international health," Pennell said, "has tremendously broadened my vision" of what the Medical Center can do for the world and for physicians who want to serve as short-term volunteers.

"I still believe that it is imperative that the Medical Center be involved in world health. We cannot cure all the world health needs or problems, but we can contribute our expertise. I think it is the responsibility of all in medicine, particularly academic and tertiary medical centers, to help with the educational needs of the nonindustrialized nations. I think it is important that we provide as much benevolent care as we can for those individuals who otherwise would not get it. I think to enlighten our students, faculty, and house staff of world health needs and the differences that exist between the industrialized and nonindustrialized countries is also an important component.

"Increasingly, I see our role not only as educating our own but also in bringing individuals from nonindustrialized nations to this country to specifically provide them with a talent, techniques, or expertise they can carry back and use in their own country.

"Aside from the moral, ethical, or personal heritage," he explained, "there are certainly no requirements that we do this and there are places that get by without any international health involvement. But I think what we've done is a reflection of our heritage." There always will be a need for mission work "because missions are people reaching out, sharing and demonstrating God's love. I don't think that will ever change."

Pennell spoke from another perspective: "When we talk about cartels and controls, we immediately think of OPEC (Organization of Petroleum Exporting Countries) and the grain cartels. We leave off the health care cartel. The truth is health care crosses cultural, political, religious, financial, and geographic boundaries. We must be ever watchful that our profession is not used as a manipulative, political tool while we are involved in services overseas."

The concept of missions, he added, must always center on sharing. Pennell, a committed Christian, over the years has shared his medical abilities, concepts of human dignity and equality, and witness "in whatever I am doing. When this works and works effectively, it gives me an easy opening to interest others in missions. That comes at the leading of the Holy Spirit. I am on duty 365 days a year, but I do not *call* anybody to missions. I do not *send* anybody to missions. I may direct, but *God* is the one who calls and sets a person apart."

He interprets God's beckon to him as a discretionary call, so he became a doer, a giver, and a healer wherever he found himself.

"As I look back at life, I realize I did not see the 'whys' at times, for I could not figure out why things were happening. But I also look back and see how things fell into place. I genuinely believe that God has a plan for us if we will just seek and follow it.

"I can remember the first hut I walked into in Africa. At the time I was with mission folks who would not go in for fear of catching something, an insult to the Nationals. I had no qualms about doing this."

Pennell went into unknown huts, dipped his hand into the yams for supper, and prayed with the Nationals, for he knew their counterparts back home, those who had taught him the universal art of communication. Long ago he grasped the shadow sides of conversation—not just what people say but what they mean and what they believe.

"If I have accomplished anything," Pennell acknowledged, "it has been based on my heritage," gained from exemplary and devoted parents and those who people the church. His earliest descriptions of the mission-bound are based on people: frail little women who wore their hair in buns, who frowned if you chewed gum, and who had a jovial nature, beaming their belief that Christians can have fun. He learned that missionaries were not "absent" people but "sent" people playing out their inner urgings.

Like old Robert, the janitor at his home church. Sometimes when the boy Tim grew weary with what was going on in the church, he would slip down to the boiler room and talk to Robert. "He was the first who began to give me some insight into the need for understanding the dignity of all men, of all people. That was valuable time."

Pennell still plays games of "hide-and-seek." When life is too taxing, answers too hidden, miracles too scarce, he slips away to the "boiler rooms" of isolation to seek insight and direction. When he could not escape, he confronted missions in his path. He started projects to meet needs. Once they caught on and other people became involved, he moved on to wherever he saw another need. Back in the 1960s, Pennell and others in the Christian Medical Society at the medical school sought to integrate their faith with their practice of medicine, viewing the two as their way of life. It was a time of ferment for people who went outside systems of authority to promote equality. Frustrated church activists became involved in secular witnessing through a social gospel.

Pennell and his fellow medical faculty, students, and personnel harnessed their energies with like-minded givers and offered a storehouse of services in the inner city. It became obvious that some people in the local community were having difficulty getting access to health care delivery. This is not to say it did not exist for them. They just did not know how to get into the system.

"We wanted to do something within our professional ability and call," Pennell said. "The time was right. We felt led to help establish what became the Downtown Church Clinic," a collaborative effort with the Downtown Church Center, Crisis Control Ministry, Forsyth County Public Health Department, and inner-city churches and members. The evening clinic allowed parents, usually hourly workers, access to medical care without the fear and risk of losing either pay or employment.

Those were days of reminiscence, he said. Volunteers often were humbled by the impact of encountering current-day Bible characters. For Pennell, it became home-front mission duty: personal confrontation with his faith and who he was in the sight of God.

Often he entered the evening clinic exhausted. More often his expertise—so vitally used during the day—was seldom truly called upon. He was needed mainly to verify for nurses whether a child was healthy enough for immunizations.

One night, while taking a smoke break on the clinic porch, he listened to the rain and wondered: "After a day like today, what am I doing down here?" That day had begun for him at 2 a.m. A teenager whose car hit a bridge abutment arrived at the hospital with his body totally smashed. His heart stopped in the emergency room, but he was resuscitated. Pennell and his team saved the youth again in surgery. Later he performed successful cancer surgery on a well-known personality. The patient's family and the state's governor were profusely thankful. And even later, he had a complex pancreatic procedure that kept him on his feet for several more hours. It had been a day of tough-and-go cases requiring his professional best. Here at day's end his volunteer services were scarcely needed.

"I felt a tug at my surgical coat. I turned around and there stood a 12-year-old holding the hand of her 4-year-old brother. She had brought him to the clinic instead of the mother who was out carousing with her boyfriend." The girl looked up at Pennell and said, "Thank you, mister"—and walked out into the damp dark night.

No matter how many times Pennell recalls that story, his voice breaks. "All of a sudden—literally—all of my priorities were rearranged. Everything else I had done that day seemed totally unimportant. That was a profound impact. Often, when I begin to get my priorities in life mismanaged, I reflect on that rainy night. If I have accomplished anything in this arena of my life, I would hope it has been to bring hope, fresh air, and new light to medical missions.

"People look to America not as the only one but the principal one to provide these basic medical needs. And people in America look to their own to do the same for them." The Medical Center continues its historic mission to provide health care to all who come for the best and for those who need the best—including those in its midst.

As more creative directions in health care are added, CPS continues its approval overlook.

Perhaps one of the finest modern examples of this outreach is the Medical Center's involvement with the former Reynolds Health Center, located on the edge of midtown Winston-Salem.

Medical school faculty, residents, and students—including Pennell—became involved in that walk-in clinic begun over a quarter of a century ago in East Winston, specifically then for the care of the black and underserved population of the county. When patients needed specialty care, they were referred to Baptist Hospital.

That care continues to this day under a new system and at a new health center.

Medical care for black residents in this city has not always been admirable, for it was not always comfortable or possible for black people to receive comprehensive medical care in public institutions prior to the Civil Rights Act.

Early in the 20th century, black physicians practiced either in their offices or in house hospitals. Later, thanks to the generosity of people interested in the welfare of blacks, Slater Hospital opened on what is now the campus of Winston-Salem State University. Black physicians took over the direction of Slater in 1908. It was sold to the state in the early 1920s.

Not only was there little money to keep Slater in operation, but black citizens willing to go to the hospital had little or no money to pay. It was a time when people who had money, blacks or whites, preferred home treatment. White doctors treated blacks in the North Wing of City Memorial Hospital in East Winston, built in 1914, a time before Baptist's emergence onto the health care scene.

In 1935 construction began on a new hospital to provide blacks with their own health care facility. Kate Bitting Reynolds Memorial Hospital opened in 1938, named after the wife of R. J. Reynolds, who founded R. J. Reynolds Tobacco Company.

The 130-bed facility was the only black hospital south of the nation's capital offering internships to black medical school graduates. "Katie B," as it was affectionately known, was a remarkable institution, considered one of the best in the state at the time.

Later, in the early 1960s, the city was faced with the problem of what to do with antiquated "Katie B" and its City Memorial Hospital, an even older facility, both in East Winston, an area fast becoming integrated and more populated by low-income families.

The politics of desegregation finally led to the abandonment of county-owned City Memorial in favor of a new facility renamed Forsyth

Memorial Hospital, located across town on the western side of the city, then almost inaccessible for poor people, black or white, who relied on public transportation. Forsyth opened in May 1964, just months before the national Civil Rights Act prohibiting discrimination.

As a countermeasure for this act of exclusion, the county built Reynolds Memorial Hospital. It opened in 1970 on the old "Katie B" site but lasted only two years, failing for the lack of financial support. The county took it over in 1975, changing its name to Reynolds Health Center. Its aim was to provide ambulatory health care of a comprehensive nature for people in East Winston, Kimberley Park, and Happy Hills, all black neighborhoods.

Baptist was among the first in the state to accept blacks at its Hawthorne Hill campus, decades before most hospitals and certainly before the Civil Rights Act. Blacks were not relegated to black-only wards, as some came to believe, for there were none. Gradually the bed occupancy was set up on a desegregated basis as it exists today.

However, the acceptance of blacks at Baptist was done in a curious manner. The patients were described on medical records as Lumbee Indians. Some physicians at the Medical Center were called to task for having more Indian patients than there were in the Lumbee Nation.

Blacks were aware of this method of admission and accepted it in order to be cared for in their times of severe illness. Physicians ignored the criticism they received for this designation, for it was their way to get entry and treatment for their patients.

In 1964, both the hospital and medical school formally adopted policies of desegregation as related to their patient care as well as for education and employment.

Baptist's involvement in caring for blacks and the underserved population of the county heightened in January 1998 when it signed an agreement with Forsyth County commissioners to take over operational responsibilities of Reynolds, one of the state's largest public health clinics, then handling over 60,000 patient visits a year.

The negotiated agreement represents a unique partnership in this state between a private medical center and a local public entity. The contractual partnership with the county and hospital became necessary when the county recognized it was not in the medical business, but it did not wish to abandon its undeniable allegiance to the care of the ill.

Taking over the clinic was a decision approved by the medical school and hospital, Pennell said. "We felt it was our responsibility to help provide care to the disadvantaged population of this community." The medical school already was providing physician services for 95 percent of the clinic's medical care, he added.

Involvement there, he said, "as it relates to indigent care and our teaching responsibilities and obligations to community-based primary care—and that's a big factor—is a continuing indication of our commitment to excellence wherever needed." The clinic, he explained, is a training ground for medical students, interns, and residents whose work is supervised by medical school faculty who work with them there.

To demonstrate its commission to serve all who are poor and sick, Baptist built a $10 million state-of-the-art health facility at 1200 Martin Luther King Jr. Boulevard, just minutes away from the old Reynolds site used for 27 years, and named it the Downtown Health Plaza of Baptist Hospital. It opened in December 2001. It is in the historic black business community now being restored and revitalized.

The new center includes an on-site pharmacy, laboratory, and radiology services. It also houses programs offered by the Department of Social Services (DSS), Women Infants and Children (WIC), Family Planning, Women and Infant Services for Health (WISH), and the Association for the Benefit of Child Development (ABCD).

The Plaza is a primary- and preventative-care facility that provides clinical services in adult internal medicine, obstetrics/gynecology, prenatal and women's health, pediatrics, and a pharmacy, clinical laboratory, X-rays, and mammography. This center also continues to offer specialty care in hypertension, neurology, surgery, renal diseases, diabetes, and ophthalmology, staffed by Wake Forest physicians and residents.

Baptist also developed the Downtown Health Plaza of Baptist Hospital Dental and Eye Center at 501 Cleveland Avenue and the Mineral Springs Dental Center of Baptist Hospital at 4850 Old Rural Hall Road. Both now offer day and evening hours for full dental services. The evening program was opened to accommodate individuals who work, attend school, or do not have transportation during day hours. In addition, elementary and middle school students in the Mineral Springs community can now receive health care at their school or the hospital can shuttle them to the clinic for dental care.

The Kate B. Reynolds Charitable Trust, Wachovia Bank, the Glenn Family Foundation, Forsyth Early Childhood Partnership, Forsyth County Health Fund, and the Winston-Salem Foundation support the Cleveland Avenue clinic. Duke Endowment is funding the Mineral Springs clinic. Both clinics are for children and others who cannot afford private dental care.

And thanks to the Ronald McDonald House Charities of North Carolina and Brenner Children's Hospital, there now is a Ronald McDonald Care Mobile dental van to further secure the possibility of youths getting proper dental care.

This up-to-date mobile dental office is defined as one of the most comprehensive vehicles of its kind in the nation, taking educational and preventative dental services into local neighborhoods to provide unmet health care needs. This outreach effort is expected to improve the health of thousands of area children who otherwise receive little dental care.

When patients at any of these facilities need extensive treatment or hospital care, they are referred to Baptist Hospital.

Under Baptist's direction, Pennell said, the Plaza is open to *all* Forsyth County residents needing medical help. Its services continue to cut across socioeconomic and cultural lines, particularly those caught in the chronic illness of being underprivileged. And the Medical Center upholds its long-standing commitment to inclusive health care in the hope that all people, not just blacks and Hispanics—the Plaza's major clients—have more equal opportunity to health care.

The hospital's vision for the Plaza includes an array of prevention and wellness programs to meet the needs of those it serves, to improve gaps in their health status so that total care is more effective and visible, and to make access to that care a possibility.

Since the early 1970s, CPS has intensified its observance of the free care Baptist Hospital has provided for the indigent. Back then patients without the means to pay often took undue advantage of the emergency department services.

It also was the season when cost containment became a medical financial buzzword and cost cutting became a voluntary procedure. By the 1990s both cost-effective moves became steadfast policies because of "thou shalts" enforced by Medicare and insurance providers.

By engaging its physicians in the former Reynolds Health program, and now at the Plaza, the Medical Center can provide quality health care for those in need at an easily accessible facility and in a more cost-beneficial way. Nearly 70 percent of the patients are covered by Medicare, Medicaid, or private coverage. The other 30 percent, who are indigent, uncovered, or unable to pay, look to the county for their medical care provided under a subsidy plan. The county pledged $15.5 million to Baptist during a five-year contractual agreement begun in 1998, dispensed in annual subsidies. In 1999, the county paid $2.6 million for the care of indigent and low-income patients.

Over the years, Pennell said, Baptist Hospital has rendered care to indigent patients and will continue to do so. Since care for indigent patients has been an integral part of the hospital's mission, he added, the federal Hill-Burton indigent care requirements were met easily through the free care program provided each year by the hospital. Free care is provided to those patients who are verified through hospital financial counseling and who lack the ability to pay and who are not otherwise eligible for sponsorship by a private or government sponsor.

Another step toward removing barriers for the underserved came in early 2002 when the medical school announced the establishment of the Maya Angelou Research Center on Minority Health. Its purpose is to equalize, by removing any disparities, the health care of all Americans, most especially for African Americans, Hispanics/Latinos, Pacific Islanders, Native Americans, and Native Alaskans. Today minorities are still less likely to receive equal medical treatment given white patients with comparable diseases.

The center will address special health issues affecting minorities by training medical students, physicians, and researchers in their major ailments and by recruiting more minority faculty members and researchers to find cures for their debilitating illnesses. The center will further involve nonwhite volunteers from Forsyth County's diverse racial population in clinical trials already targeted by the medical school: infant mortality, cancer screening and management, cardiovascular diseases, diabetes, HIV infections, and child and adult immunizations—health hazards minorities especially face.

The project will be conducted in partnership with Winston-Salem State University, historically a black state institution, and other local organizations in the hope of creating an appropriate working model for other American communities on how to eliminate racial and ethnic health disparities.

Two founding grants—$500,000 from the Duke Endowment and $80,000 from the Winston-Salem Foundation—will help initiate the center named for Angelou, an internationally known poet, author, civil rights activist, and Reynolds Professor of American Studies at Wake Forest University. She will serve on the center's steering committee along with other civil rights and peace advocates and medical leaders.

The Medical Center, Pennell said, keeps spreading more home-front missions in many ways, making public health services more accessible. He noted a few:

• The 15 **Aegis Family Health Centers**R located in and around Winston-Salem were awarded accreditation with commendation by JCAHO in January 2000. These freestanding clinics, subsidiaries of Baptist Hospital, were begun in 1994 and provide the same high-quality primary-care health care services to patients in the community and in the Northwest North Carolina region as available at Baptist Hospital.

• **Amos Cottage and Developmental Evaluation Clinic** has changed its primary approach from inpatient residential care of children with physical, mental, and emotional handicaps to outpatient clinics and services for these developmental disabilities. However, the medical school will continue to offer inpatient hospitalization support for those in need in a six-bed wing located in the new Brenner Children's Hospital. Going to an outpatient focus will allow the staff to help more patients and their families through evaluations, diagnoses, and referrals for rehabilitation programs, particularly with autism, cerebral palsy, mental rehabilitation, severe attention deficit disorder, and deficit sight and hearing abilities.

• **The Nursing Center at Oak Summit** was opened by Baptist Hospital in 1993 when it realized it had patients who needed continuing specialized care. These patients had not been able to leave the hospital because they had no place to relocate. The Center scored 98 on its first accreditation survey by JCAHO. The 170-bed skilled nursing and intermediate-care facility is located on a separate campus north of the city.

• Baptist Hospital now uses **telemedicine** as a vital force and available source for assisting with diagnostic and emergency problems occurring in its increased partnership with other Northwest North Carolina hospitals. Physicians and caregivers outside the county can enhance their effectiveness by telephone connection with Medical Center specialists to discuss patient needs, review treatment options, and seek opinions on transmitted technological findings, thus saving lives and money. And patients can use this approach, regarded as the 21st century's answer to house calls or tel-home care, as their lifelines at the end of a phone-computer line.

• Baptist Hospital opened the state's first mall-based community health information center, **BestHealth**SM, in Winston-Salem. There visitors can get a free check of their blood pressure, learn from special classes on nutrition and exercise, hear speakers outline good health practices, get health and medical questions answered by registered nurses, and introduce their kids to **Brenner Children's Corner** and the **BestHealthKids**SM **Club**. Also available are special health screenings, such as hearing tests and stroke assessments; an informational library of books, audio, and videotapes; and limited Internet access about health.

It has been a meeting place for the popular annual mini-medical school community education programs sponsored by the Medical Center. The 2002 series dealt with genetics, radiology, cancer, cardiology, and physiology and pharmacology. Also popular is **BestHealth's** good health cooking classes.

BestHealth.com is a popular website for health information, and **For Your BestHealth** is featured on cable television in both Winston-Salem/Forsyth County and Greensboro with health-related issues being explained by Medical Center staff.

• The medical school and hospital in September 2000 purchased the former Charter Behavioral Health System in Winston-Salem, which had closed. The three-building campus was named **Wake Forest University Baptist Behavioral Health Inc**. Extensive renovations have been made. The not-for-profit corporation provides inpatient and partial hospitalization behavioral services. Administrative operations and the first program, "Second Beginnings," a residential treatment program for sexually aggressive children and adolescents, got underway in April 2001. To meet the educational needs of these young people, WFUBBH opened a licensed private school at the Old Vineyard Road site in October 2001. Currently WFUBBH has a total of 45 beds for these young residents with special needs. In March 2002, "Journeys," an adolescent day treatment and partial hospitalization program, opened with a capacity for 16 children or adolescents. This program cares for those clients and families previously served by a Charter Hospital program that closed in March 2002. A 20-bed residential program for older adults with substance abuse problems opened in June 2002.

• The Medical Center continues its **Northwest Area Health Education Center (AHEC)**, sponsoring a variety of programs for health professionals in 17 Northwest counties. It offered training to nearly 17,000 students in 2001. AHEC's programs are for the benefit of a diverse health care workforce employed in the area.

• The Medical Center has a telephone **Call Center** that is an answering service for area and local physicians' offices, health information from medical informants, and referral services for consumers. It began in 1989 with **PAL**[R], Physicians' Access Line, a toll-free line for physicians in the region for immediate access to specialists and subspecialists at the Medical Center. A second telephone service, **Health On-Call**[R], started in 1991 as a health information and physician appointment service for Forsyth County residents. In this new century, patients are turning to their computers for Internet health information, but Medical Center caregivers warn that answers to their questions are not always complete or reliable, so they suggest that patients click with care. With the Medical Center's Call Centers, full help is available.

As the Medical Center's health care missions continue to radiate out from Hawthorne Hill in increasingly new and creative ways, the Medical Center's core mission is still to make known its call and commitment to benefit people both sick and well.

And its world-class capabilities in preeminent academic tertiary care offer hope that is becoming increasingly more inclusive.

XV   NOT-FOR-PROFIT MANAGED CARE

Wake Forest University Baptist Medical Center, a not-for-profit institution, has been in the managed care health business since its inception. And that dates to an era in modern medicine when health care was managed to fully benefit patients.

Now 61 years later, people who do not see or know the patients are managing more and more of Wake Forest's health care business, a national trend. It is not unlike the game where the child asks: "May I take three giant steps?"

More often for-profit institutions known as health maintenance organizations (HMOs) give the giant-step answer, and it is not always, "Yes, you can." They even may ask, "Is this treatment necessary?" Or they may respond, "You didn't say 'May I?'" which is part of their game, meaning, "You didn't get prior approval from your primary care doctor."

Americans, individuals and businesses, spend more money on health care delivery than any other nation in the world, but the end product, many Americans will tell you, is not now always in their best interest.

Forty-two years ago Pennell and his fellow graduating seniors were told by their commencement speaker that patients must become persons for whom they were personally responsible in the medical chain of care.

Pennell recalled this when he spoke at the 1999 "Hooding Ceremony" at Wake Forest University School of Medicine. He told that gathering to be patients' ombudsmen and fight for what they need to get well and to stay well. This might include, he added, "the system, the Medical Center, the insurance carriers, whatever it took to properly care for patients.

"The concept of 'my patient' was driven into all of us in the profession then. We carried this through the years." With this in mind, he continued, "think of what all has transpired in these past four decades." He listed unbelievable technological changes and advancements and treatment modalities: CAT and MRI scans; virtual reality; the entire field of laparoscopic surgery and noninvasive procedures; absolute cures in some cancers; immunosuppression leading to heart, liver, lungs, and bone marrow transplants; angioplastics; genetic mapping;

and "that horrendous Pandora's box of AIDS." The list, he added, goes on and on and includes additions in every field and branch of medicine.

"America's medicine has truly climbed to the pinnacle and has become recognized as the best health care in the world," he said. "But someone woke up one morning and said, 'My God, look at this: Eleven percent plus of our gross national product (GNP)—that's higher than most any other country—is going for health care. We cannot afford that. We have got to control this. That wild bunch of overpaid doctors is ruining us!'

"Then came managed care with its unbelievable alphabet soup: PPOs, HCFA, HMOs, et cetera. All of these remain in the bowl. Some have fallen to the bottom, others have layered out, and those that remain on the surface are glaring at us daily.

"Rather suddenly, we were forced to transition from 'my' patient to 'our' patient. We are faced with all types of external controls and managers, and we are forced to be a part of the very systems that we have been fighting," Pennell explained.

"If it is just the increasing complexity of health care and all those myriad of dynamics, such as regulatory oversight, required paperwork and documentation, and a more experienced and specialized administration," he said, "then that is valid."

If there weren't some kind of medical insurance system in place to help level out the cost factor, he continued, the Medical Center and all health caregiving facilities across the nation could not survive, for there always will be those individuals who are unable to pay-as-they-go for health care. Thankfully, he added, more people today are insured and that facilitates their access to health care.

"Managed care," he said, "is not going away," so its system's position is taught to medical students, for it will be their medical obligation "to help these external groups to be mindful that health care is provided to biological systems—not mechanical ones."

Medicine's focus must be on "our fellow human beings," Pennell told the graduates. Patients are not just people passing through or the insured. "They are biological systems that are complex," so physicians "must be in charge of this component and their care," developing for them "care maps, decision aids, and the basis and means for continuing improvement in quality care."

At this time, he continued, "the greatest and probably the only thing going for you physicians will be outcomes research: the capability to prove that your care is better and less costly—especially in the long run—because you are better and your system is better. This means you have got to be honest and objective: no rationalization or deception, especially of self. Our basic scientists and other researchers have given you insight here. You must prove that the severity of your patient's illness is higher and that the series of tests, procedures, or modes of treatment will pay off."

Medicine has always encountered ethical dilemmas, he allowed, so this insurance dilemma is not totally new. Under managed care's governance, physicians must measure and then weigh, must determine and then warrant, must decide and then proceed with what *they* feel is in the best interest of their patients, so he advocated following proven outcomes research as the grail in their honored treatment of their patients.

He further advocated that the graduates practice and apply three concepts he followed in medicine—regardless of "your religious background, beliefs, or lack thereof." He offered this resolve: "Bless every patient or person you encounter." But be aware, he added, "that it is a two-edged sword. Accept *your* blessings with humility, gratitude, graciousness, and determination." Comfort somebody everyday, he added, and "'Do unto others as you would have them do unto you.' Do these things, my young friends, and you will lead us to the next and higher levels and planes of managed care."

The highest level of medicine traditionally, morally, and ethically, Pennell said, has been to provide total care dispensed with compassion, cure sought after complete disease assessment, wellness maintained through assertive clinical intervention.

Understandably, this treatment mode—whether in a doctor's office or a hospital—cannot be obtained without a price tag, he said. The profession does not like to be labeled as a money-making business but rather as a decision-making practice that profits patients' health.

It is the monetary aspect, however, that caused insurance dispensers to vacate their phantom role in medicine to become pharisaical profit-makers in the name of health. It was a gainful decision.

For medicine, it caused health caregivers to question what happened to their authority to practice their profession. Recent national surveys report how some doctors got around that problem. They couched causes of major health-compromising illnesses in terms that automatically got authorized insurance coverage and best-quality care for their patients under managed care plans. These doctors admitted their decisions were necessary in order to bypass restrictions made by insurance providers. The contest became necessary, they said, if they were going to stabilize patients' health and their own reimbursement income. No Medical Center physicians were indentified in this national survey.

For patients, it caused them to question what happened to healing availability, a provision they had grown up with and depended on when their health was in disarray. They are confused with insurance providers over "who pays what" and with medical providers who let collection agencies turn up the pressure for payments.

The financing of health care began about a 100 years ago, but it was not until 1973 that a federal law opened the way for insurance companies to compete within the health care coverage industry. The cost of medical care began to rise in the 1960s, mostly in hospitals, due to expensive new equipment increasingly needed in treatment and prevention procedures. Private insurance, government insurance or aid, or patients' out-of-pocket money paid for these services.

Today about 80 percent of Americans have some form of health coverage, either from personal insurance policies, health maintenance organizations, federal programs, or employer-provided benefits. Usually patients make percentage payments for their health care cost, the rest being absorbed by their various insurance providers.

The largest public health care program is the federal Medicare plan, which helps those usually age 65 and over to pay for outpatient and hospital care. Medicaid provides medical care subsidies for many people unable to pay for medical services.

The most common health care plans are HMOs, dating to the 1930s but progressively more active since the 1970s, and preferred provider organizations (PPOs), a more flexible plan, which entered the health care competition market in the 1980s.

Members of HMOs use only authorized physicians and hospitals, selected for their cost-effectiveness. These providers further reduce costs by favoring outpatient rather than inpatient care. They also carefully determine need and permission for hospitalization or to go to specialists.

Members of PPOs also select preferred doctors and hospitals; however, their clients may go outside this list by paying higher fees.

In today's medicine, treatment often begins with managed care's prescribed remedy: Downsize assessment, care, and compassion, all in the name of saving money. While it helped force medicine to adopt cost-effective measures, medicine still strives within these restrictions to provide the best and latest in quality, technological health care delivery, a decision it made on its own without any prodding from insurance providers.

The Medical Center's prescription is managing diseases to benefit patients. This approach is cost-productive because it often can prevent extensive and expensive complications and can keep patients' health on a more even keel. Its disease management programs address chronic illnesses, like asthma, congestive heart failure, depression, diabetes, and hypertension. Intervention often can halt or delay long-term risks.

Wake Forest and Baptist Hospital in an effort to provide patients with quality health care and for the Medical Center to maintain a continuing basis of patients began their own managed care insurance plan in 1994. QualChoice of North Carolina, solely owned by the hospital, served customers primarily in central and western North Carolina and more specifically employees of Wake Forest University and the Medical Center. However, this plan was dissolved at year-end 2002 due to conflicts presented by simultaneously owning an HMO and treating patient members of the HMO. The hospital continues MedCost, another managed care company it jointly owns with Carolinas HealthCare Systems of Charlotte.

"If we destroy our patient-referral base or if patients don't want to come here because they are not pleased with the care they get here or the doctors aren't rendering the kind of service expected and wanted," Pennell said, then the Medical Center could face new financial woes.

There is also the possibility, he added, "that other insurance companies will do like Partners Health Plan, which does not pay for its patients to go to the Medical Center for most tertiary care services or even to other academic medical centers in the state. That means our patient-referral base is harmed and we are out again. That patient base is what this whole game of insurance is about."

Above the current din of anger and frustration in medicine hangs this query: "Who should control medical care? The physicians, the patients, or the payers?"

The answer is intricate. The answer is all three.

For "choosing the best" costs, Pennell said. Medicine is trying to hold onto its profession as full-scale and not cut-rate; patients are trying to find more-caring rather than less-caring caregivers; and insurance payers are trying to define "shared authority."

For the vast majority of medical care institutions, making money is not their first premise, and this is certainly true at this Medical Center, but profit making is a necessary means to fulfilling its mission.

In times past, physicians, hospitals, and other health care providers were paid by private or federal health insurance for services rendered, Pennell explained. Under managed care plans, these same providers are paid by prearranged and discounted fee-for-services plans: They agree to accept preset fees for particular services or treatments. In an arrangement called "capitation," providers are paid flat monthly fees for individual patients enrolled in managed care plans—regardless of what the monthly services might entail or cost.

The premise is that most patients will not dip into their "health accounts" monthly; therefore, their "banked" surplus will be available to cover high-service users. In the long run, the banked funds will balance out between the light and heavy users.

Under capitation, medical providers are encouraged to reduce unnecessary and costly care and tests on their patients, but they see this as an ethical conflict of interest. If they don't go along with the plans, however, they stand to lose that income. Their income depends on insured patients.

Managed care contracts often demand that more patients be scheduled daily and patient visits be limited to about 10 minutes each, which, if followed, can cripple physician-patient relationships, trust, and full review of health maintenance. Doctors hate hurry-up harassment. Studies show that physicians now spend about 20 minutes per patient visit because today's illnesses are more complicated.

Denying care is alien to physicians, Pennell said, but so is being denied income reimbursement.

Physicians now must go beyond answering if their procedures are necessary or if their treatment is cost-practical to asking if their decisions will be detrimental to their income potential. If they lower costs, patients' insurance providers may reward physicians with rebate pay.

So does that mean that very sick patients are shunned? Does that explain some physicians' dislike of the critically or chronically ill? Are these patients a financial liability to their physicians? Has medicine become a power broker first? Have insurance providers become merely power structures? Are patients leaving managed care health plans—as are doctors—because they are powerless in their health care decisions?

These very distasteful propositions hang like clothes on a line: clearly visible, awaiting the next step. The total profession must engage in unpinning these articles of concern: distrust, resentment, penny-pinching, and no-fault compassion.

Perhaps the greatest responsibility in this *Catch-22* difficulty rests with physicians. Today they must be more than doctors: They must be efficiency experts, efficient businesspersons, and efficacious merchant-specialists—and maybe all they ever wanted to be was effective at healing and acquainted with compassion and truth.

They resent being told by HMOs what treatments they can prescribe, what patients they can accept—the healthy but not the older and sicker—and who they can refer to specialists. Many now refuse to accept managed care and Medicare patients in their practice and their hospitals.

Academic medical centers are at stake, too. They are feeling severe monetary losses due to HMOs failing to financially support clinical training for future doctors—much like the federal government's reduction of medical education support. And they are feeling the squeeze of inadequate reimbursements by Medicare and Medicaid patients.

Patients are searching for low-cost health care networks in an effort to bypass managed care's grip on the market and on them. Both patients and institutions are seeking ways to ease their financial and health woes without dipping into reserve funds.

Some HMOs, wanting to hold down costs, will reward their contract physicians if they do. Now some HMOs are increasing that reward as they seek both patient satisfaction and physician contentment.

HMOs also have reduced their participation in Medicare, citing insufficient reimbursement rates set by Congress. Because they are experiencing lower earnings than expected, as well as rising medical care costs, most HMOs in 2002 increased plan costs to cover this increase.

All participants in the management of health care are beginning to acknowledge that they are not each other's enemy.

Pennell, speaking from his heritage as physician and chief, believes federal insurance programs will be restructured within another decade or so, depending on lawmakers' campaign promises. He foresees a decrease in Medicare and an expansion of Medicaid programs. "But I think it will take time to arrive at that," he added, and it may be that states will take over more in managing federal coverage.

He also believes that in the future patients' personal wealth will determine the amount of support the government will grant them in medical care. Each illness, he feels, will have a different pathway of management and this is when outcomes research will be of extreme importance to the full dispensation of care.

"This is going to be a trade-off that medicine does not like but that business will demand," Pennell said, and the demand is the best return on the dollar.

Pennell also believes that companies offering cheap plans for health maintenance will increase. "And I think that's when industries and purchasers of health care will wake up and realize that quality does mean something and that individuals with the best outcomes research, best outcomes, lowest morbidity, lowest mortality, et cetera, will get the health care business even if they are a bit more costly."

As for uninsured Americans, Pennell said, "I am not sure how this is going to turn out. I can envision it being a regionalization of health care, whereby federal money is designated as subsidy to regions of a state for programs providing health care to the uninsured."

He further believes the greatest need in the health care industry at this turning point in history "is for the dust to settle on the HMO industry, Medicaid, Medicare, and the whole issue of reimbursement. There is no doubt in my mind that this is the greatest need."

It is of utmost importance, he added, that the trust relationships between patients and physicians not be undermined in the process of creating more effective medical care.

There are those who disagree, Pennell admitted, but he sees medicine benefiting as it undergoes this current walk through the development of health care management. "We needed some checks and balances on this; therefore, I am not altogether upset about it because I still feel it is possible to work within this system," providing what is right and appropriate for patients.

"I think this may be good for medicine because I think not only is it going to bring around cost-containment, it will stop some of the pocket-feathering—putting money into one's own pocket. This is where businesspeople have abused us: Some guy comes in and says, 'Here's how to maximize what you can get out of each patient.'

"What I am talking about is programmed managed care," he said, whereby programmed outlines for the best management of patients' treatment needs are in place to follow. "I think this has real benefits. I think that case management, when set up by the right persons and the right groups of persons, is not all bad.

"A lot of changes are taking place in medicine today, and I think a lot of them are good. I think they are good, first and foremost, for the patient and they are good for the profession as well."

Over the years Pennell witnessed other changes, notably the growth of excellence at the Medical Center. "It is a staggering phenomenon. I think we have done well in calculating the brick-and-mortar growth as it relates to the expansion" of the Hawthorne campus. "We still need space and buildings. Back in the 1950s and 1960s, we questioned whether we should expand any more on this site or if we should move to Graylyn (now Wake Forest University's conference center). We agreed this is where we should remain.

"Next came the growth in faculty, academic standings, and national research, and this has been even more staggering. A lot of our growth has bubbled up from the bottom to the top, and we expanded to meet this new growth. For example, look at the development of the bone-marrow transplant program, the regional and state trauma-registry system, and the significant areas in basic science and other research we are doing." He also listed how well medical students perform on national board exams, the quality of students admitted, and increased NIH funding.

"All of these growth factors have been great," he said, and have been done for the maintenance and stability needed for clinical excellence, teaching, and patient care.

Despite these successes, he added, "there are those out there really trying to hurt us: government leaders, HMO insurances, and other third-party gatekeepers. Our incomes are down and costs continue to go up. Yet the opportunities are still here for our patients to get as good health care delivery as there is in the world for virtually any problems they have and it is delivered with skill and compassion.

"Now this is not to say that the Medical Center doesn't have problems because we do. But we do try to identify them and correct them. We have an outside agency that surveys patients and their contentment level with us, and we have scored well above the national norm in all areas for a long time—except in food, which we have corrected. We also survey our employees routinely. It basically is a good place to work with better-than-average fringe benefits, competitive salaries, and a good work environment.

"Our biggest problem is with faculty compensation, and next is the rate and speed of faculty promotions. As it relates to economic rewards, in comparison to most medical centers, we have done very well—basically because we have an incentive program in which the harder you work, the more you are paid.

"What will be our direction for the next couple of decades? I honestly don't know. It depends on whether the government will fairly compensate teaching and training institutions. That remains a big issue. If they don't, increasingly we will see medical schools in the nation closing and going under—and that already is happening but not here. The board of trustees at Wake Forest University decides the future and fate of the medical school as recommended by the medical school leadership. There is no effort under way to close the school—not unless it becomes such a financial burden for the university that it could not survive.

"We will see hospitals with training programs cutting back or cutting them out. Fortunately, that is not happening here. The hospital board of trustees decides its future. But the hospital could not exist without the medical school faculty or vice versa. So we are in this together."

Neither institution can consider buying out the other, if it were possible, he said, so the Medical Center continues its massive realignment, shoring up its future "because there are a lot of outside players who are trying to decide our future," he said.

Pennell has been the chief most active in assisting the Medical

Center to think and act as a unified institution. It has been a focus of his throughout his medical career. He wanted accomplishments recognized not as a success from either the hospital or medical school but from the Medical Center as a unified whole. That oneness level is closer than it ever has been because of his political ability to help both sides understand each other's missions.

While legal restraints for total unity are incredible enough, he said, the basic problem is this: "The hospital is a business whereas the medical school is not. The medical school survives on tuition, fees, grants, endowments, et cetera, whereas the hospital exists on revenue earned in the care of the patients it serves."

As it goes through realignment, the Medical Center maintains its continuum core mission: to continue being the true managed care health provider for its patients.

Physicians and staff continue to stand by their calling to protect and care for their patients.

And more responsible insurance providers are beginning to reconsider and recognize physicans' right to self-determinism.

XVI   21ST CENTURY MEDICAL ADVANCEMENTS

The Medical Center's accomplishments have brought people closer to disease- and pain-free existence and to a longer and often more pleasurable life because deadly diseases have been held in check by vaccines and therapies, by more minutely exact surgeries, by more easily replaced organs, and by more second use of cells.

Medicine in the future perfect, Pennell explained, will become even more of a genius at making transplants adhere, curing or halting cancer, operating without incisions, reversing impotence and obesity, making new heart muscles and tissues, and further unscrambling the mysteries of the body's switchboard, the genetic code.

Medicine is expected in this millennium to capture more clues from the blood-rich placenta, to scientifically create a pancreas or a brain or a new heart—or regenerate their cells—and increasingly use inhalants to dispense medications and vaccines.

As the century ages, medicine will endeavor to perfect artificial limbs and custom-designed babies, treat devastating inherited blemishes through gene altering, heal fractures and slipped vertebrae with putty-like substances to promote bone growth and restoration, and develop pacemaker-like devices to make organs work more dependably.

Medicine will introduce mind-over-matter approaches to control dysfunction without personality-altering drugs and teach patients how to use the heart and brain in harmony to restrain stress.

Another major giant step in future medicine, Pennell said, will be the increased use of stem cells to repair the body's tissues. At the moment, he added, that research is under criticism by antiabortionists who oppose fetal and embryonic stem-cell research made possible from aborted fetuses and fertility clinic discards. Usually, he said, leftover cells are destroyed, but researchers are trying to recapture the potential use of certain master cells to bring recovery to millions suffering from Alzheimer's, Huntington's, and Parkinson's diseases, as well as regenerating human tissues either paralyzed or dead, in an effort to reverse the progression of these diseases.

The human body's master cells, or stem cells, offer the possibility of diversifying into any one of the body's over 200 cell types. That discovery is needed for replacement tissues and organs to treat 100 million patients now in the nation with organ diseases. Stem cells can be obtained from embryos, fetal tissues, adult tissues, and experimental cells being grown in laboratories. Stem cells alone, however, cannot form a human life.

On the stem cell matter, Pennell said, medicine and morality can clash, for it is a subject on which many have definite opinions, but then religion and science often work together. Medical Center stem cell research, like all its research, he added, is pursued under strict ethical and moral guidelines and monitored by CPS and departmental leadership.

Nationally, organs are now harvested at the moment of death for transplantation. Extra embryos from *in vitro* fertilization could be used for the creation of stem cells for new organs. Most scientists back research on embryonic and adult cell colonies and hope that future research will lead to patients' own cells healing tissues damaged from disease and injury.

With the Bush Administration's policy announcement in August 2001, this molecular biology issue has moved from ethics to equity.

The administration is limiting federal research only to 64 designated human embryonic stem cell lines. Many are questioning this limited quantity and, perhaps, quality, viability, and purity. Scientists feel the policy hampers their potential as researchers to find therapies to treat and cure ailing patients who need regenerative medical intervention.

Scientists accepting federal grants for regenerative research must follow stated government protocol and NIH's oversight. Cells extracted by the August 2001 cutoff were the only ones eligible for study. These cells are leftover from *in vitro* fertility treatment. Federal funding will not apply to any new cells created. Private scientists are free to continue their private research if using private funding; however, scientists fear that accepting private support could jeopardize receiving future federal grants.

Experienced researchers at academic centers, such as those at the Medical Center, will likely be the recipients of available NIH funding for authorized embryonic stem cell research.

Here in the new millennium, it is a time to wonder about other wonders and other discoveries, and scientists and clinicians are doing just that, for they will be making major decisions regarding the treatment and care of patients.

And CPS will nurture and safeguard these second-sighted wonderings.

The aid of many skilled medical providers will be needed for medicine's future team efforts at curing, Pennell said. Hospitals like Baptist will need to continue doing their very best at treating those patients who depend on their recognized care, their proven safety measures, their highly successful and credentialed specialty procedures.

And insurance providers will need to continue guiding their patients to this Medical Center because they have screened its health care providers, pronounced them as the best, and found them accredited and licensed and working under disciplinary standards.

Patients may feel caught in future shock, unable to cope with the rapidity of medical and technological changes, Pennell said, but they want future's possibilities as present-day availabilities. Physicians and caretakers understand this, for they are students of futurology: future possibilities based on current trends.

From his panoramic experience as a physician and a medical leader, Pennell made some observations about medicine's destiny.

He would like medicine to restore its longtime pledge "to put the needs and concerns of patients first—without financial considerations or limitations—and decide what needs to be done for patients and how to put them at ease with their fears and apprehension about that care.

"I believe in the future everything is going to be pushed further and further into an outpatient or ambulatory care arena. I still think that 5 or maybe 10 percent of most surgeries done in inpatient facilities could be handled on an ambulatory basis with some expansion of capabilities.

"What you are confronted with in outpatient care surgery are the charges and allegations against procedures such as 'drive-through' mastectomies. That became a rallying word for a lot of women's groups who felt this was grossly inappropriate and grossly unfair. Yet, at the same time, most of my patients—and I certainly did lumpectomies—I sent home the same day. And most mastectomy patients *wanted* to go home by the next day. But there are those groups who are opposed to this and say it's done because it is not male surgery. So, here again, educating the public is an important component for understanding this.

"Insurance companies have declared a number of diagnostic-related groups (DRGs) in which they will cover procedures only for x-number of days, and this is where the fight about discharging a mother and baby within 24 hours after delivery—*if both are healthy*—came from.

"There will be insurance companies that will pay for one day of hospitalization following mastectomy. Hernias are another example. At least 60 to 80 percent of all hernia patients probably can be discharged from the operating room after they have recovered. They do not need to be admitted. Those who cannot be discharged immediately include the older male who has trouble with his prostate and cannot void or patients who cannot tolerate pain. But the greatest majority, if there's someone at home to get their meals for them and to watch over them, can be. "When I first started in surgery, after you repaired a hernia, the patient would be in the hospital for a minimum of three days and usually five days in bed. That's one of the dramatic changes.

"Today anything that decreases the stay in the hospital is to the advantage of the institution and the insured and those who provide care. This is where I think physicians have to be ombudsmen for their patients. More and more patients are being managed on an ambulatory basis: same-day surgery, day hospital, one night stays. The length of stay is how you contain cost, improve care, make more money, et cetera, for the institution."

The length of stay is a very important indicator, he said, and CPS pays close attention to this, trying to focus efforts on better patient management to decrease it. "Although we know our patients are more acutely ill than average, we believe there is opportunity to reduce their stay and to move toward the statewide average of 5.5 days (not including obstetrics).

"We are committed to do so without compromising care. We increasingly are practicing evidence-based medicine that improves both outcomes of care and efficiency. Reducing extent of stay is becoming critical to our effort to respond to increasing demand, within the limited resources of facilities and staffing.

"The biggest role for general surgery in the future will continue to be trauma—not only big and massive surgeries but also multisystem injuries where the surgeon is involved with vascular, orthopaedic, GYN, and GI tract injuries.

"I don't think there is any doubt that we are doing more aggressive, more invasive procedures on sicker people. Yet the paradox is that we also do less-invasive procedures through laparoscopy, where you take out the gallbladder without opening the abdomen, and arthroscopy, where you take cartilage out of the knee or examine the insides of organs or cavities in the body."

Medicine needs to rethink the total issue of transplantation and organ donations, Pennell said, "and this has the potential of becoming another real political dilemma. We have to create a situation and an environment in which organ procurement is enhanced and expanded— even accepting organs from the elderly—and then determine how distribution will take place," for the demands for organs keep increasing as do medical techniques to preserve and reuse donated organs.

Some advocate the legalization of buying organs and black market sales, mostly from cadavers. The number of organs available from deceased donors has slowed, while the number from living donors has more that doubled and the number of people on transplant waiting lists is increasing more than ever in the history of transplantation.

The government, he said, is developing a national uniform organ transplant network whereby the sickest patients awaiting transplantation will be the first beneficiaries. But the plan, he added, does not address the geographical problem, meaning donated organs remain in the areas given, which could result in a waste of scarce organs if they are not promptly used or if there is no patient match.

The greatest need for the estimated 75,000 people on organ waiting lists, Pennell said, is for liver and kidney transplants, followed by hearts, lungs, and pancreases. Most waiting will likely remain there for some time. The national waiting list has grown by 10 percent yearly for the past decade. The number of deaths of people on the waiting list has more than tripled.

Pennell and others have made unified pleas for more people to become donors. In essence, he said, it's a matter of renewed public education about organ need. He encouraged people to make known their desires to be organ donors by signing cards confirming this.

"We need to seek permission from families of any young trauma deaths or any other young deaths so that the individuals can become organ donors. We will probably arrive some day at the point where this will be mandated.

"I think confining transplants to x-number of medical centers is an extremely important concept. I don't think every state or certainly every medical school or major hospital in every state, for example, ought to be doing liver transplants. There is a learning curve there that's necessary or otherwise organs are wasted."

Organ transplant surgery, he added, is difficult, involved, meticulous, and exhausting for doctors, for often surgeons must also address other bodily abnormalities.

The Medical Center's heart transplant program opened in 1993, Pennell said, and is one of only four in the state and one of 89 in the nation where Medicare will pay for this surgery. The Medical Center's one-year survival rate for these transplant patients is 94 percent as compared to the national average of 85 percent.

At present Medical Center surgeons have not transplanted the newest mechanical heart, but they realize that this latest plastic invention could be the miracle so many need. They know, too, that while it could continue life, it will not be a simple procedure.

Heart transplant surgery is getting nearer to becoming routine as researchers worldwide are "growing" heart parts, such as heart muscle, in their laboratories, as well as valves, arteries, and nerve tissues. Within a decade, Pennell said, these off-the-shelf parts could be a reality, relieving the need for many donor organs.

Technology will play a larger role, too, in future heart surgery other than transplant operations, Pennell said. Surgeons can now operate on patients by computer, telling surgical robots what procedures to do. In the distant future, he added, surgeons will be able routinely to do heart bypass, for instance, without opening the chest or stopping the heart. This is not in use at the Medical Center, he explained, but it's likely to be added in time, as physicians become more technologically experienced. This type of corrective surgery is less traumatic for the patient.

Heart specialists of the future also will be able to do long-distance robotic surgery, staying at their home-base office while patients remain in their remote hometown hospital. But at-distance surgery faces the problems of power or signal failures, licensing, and ability of hometown surgeons to intervene should procedures fail.

Improvements in sight and hearing will continue in the future, Pennell said. "Hearing aids are getting smaller. But nerve deafness is still nerve deafness, and I don't know what is being done in that particular arena. I think unequivocally that cataract surgery has significantly improved and is accepted, but as I learned from my professors, postcataract vision is different and will not take patients back to their 30-year-old vision. Cataract glasses and implants improve sight, but patients still have postcataract vision.

"I think the care of the diabetic eye has improved with retina surgery, and there have been significant strides in the treatment of glaucoma and this will continue."

There are still major illnesses that plague medicine and humans today, Pennell said, "and diabetes has got to be one of them and cancer is another. And then there are the inflammatory bowel disorders (Crohn's disease and ulcerative colitis), and all the mental health disorders," which disturb individuals' behavior, thinking, and emotions and "why people do what they do."

Here again, he said, it is the physician relying on research and the development of new drugs. "As an institution, we do not pay people to be a part of our research testing, but the grant that allows us to do the testing may. Trial periods can last from six months to over two years."

One of the most lifesaving and lifemending drugs, he said, "is insulin for diabetics. Pain relievers are another. Antibiotics are another as are some of the cancer agents. Then you have the female hormones as they relate to osteoporosis. Drugs for atherosclerosis. And antiseizure agents. These are all life-enhancing."

One of the pain relievers so often used, aspirin, is the oldest and least expensive of the over-the-counter analgesics, but it can be a problem in surgery, Pennell said. "People take it to keep from getting strokes and this type of thing, but it keeps patients' blood from clotting when you operate on them. So the bottom line before an operation is to ask, 'Are you taking aspirin or any medications that contain aspirin?' This same thing is true for ulcer patients or patients who are bleeding from their gut."

Major advancements in drug therapy have evolved since the late 1940s, Pennell said. But drug procurement for some patients still means deciding whether to eat properly or to buy medications that sustain life, for some health plans do not cover their needs. Prescription drug cost is increasing three times faster than health care services, he added. For the uninsured, hope often lies with those who offer free medicines, be they inner-city clinics, goodwill and faith-based ministries, or physician and pharmaceutical samples.

Major improvements in drug availability, Pennell believes, will continue to plague medicine until politicians begin to hear their constituents and then work to correct this inequity in health care.

A current trend, and one likely to increase, is patient use of the Internet to access e-health information and then demand these offerings—whether appropriate or not—from their caretakers on the next scheduled health care visits. Pennell feels physicians should make the first health decisions, for they are more knowledgeable about accredited medical treatment, therapies, and alternatives.

They also know that their diagnoses begin first with patients rather than diseases, and when they communicate their findings to the patient, they must be in clear and understandable language.

Future advancements at the Medical Center, Pennell said, always will include new construction, rehabilitation of old structures, newer precautions in medical computer strategies and patient confidentiality, and the latest and proven equipment to save lives, time, and expense.

In the Medical Center's earliest days, he remembered, the campus was small and lean. But as its services increased, expansion became necessary. Today, he added, "by arrangement we have services geographically clustered to allow for improved care of patients. You can provide better specialized care and services when you have specialized people with special interests, such as with burns—and we do need a new burn unit—trauma, pediatrics, general medicine, oncology, et cetera, all concentrated by special interest. Then, too, physicians don't have to walk all over God's green earth just to see their patients.

"In essence, what we are doing now is restructuring our medical complex and at the same time updating the facilities and modernizing with accompanying technologies—not unlike what you do at your home when you update it. We will come out of this phase with slightly more available beds and a higher percentage will be private rooms. We have not had as large a number of private beds as some other places, but we will go to about an 80 percent private bed mix. One of the keys to this is to make swing beds where you can make single rooms double when you need them. Most patients want single rooms, but then there are those who prefer not to be alone.

"The time has come," he added, to consider "how much larger we should grow. We cannot be—and should not be—the best in everything. There is no way we can be. Being bigger does not necessarily mean being better. But what we need to do is define what we want to do and where we want to be the best. We are running out of campus space."

Those who serve the Medical Center agree it no longer can be a charitable institution or hospital, for it has grown from a community server to a major institution recognized internationally for its medical competence, quality, and sweeping abilities.

Because of its size, Pennell said, its leadership must protect its financial footings against outsiders reducing their reimbursement promises, leaving the Medical Center with lessened monetary returns and caregivers with unpredictable cash flow and lower fees for services.

Many realize—along with Pennell—that the time has come when the hospital must maintain appreciation for its past if it is to provide guidance in the future for those it is committed to serve.

Pennell saluted the handful of people who get the Medical Center ready every three years "so that we come out of our accreditation review with approval." Pennell remains in awe when "catastrophic events happen and they are addressed appropriately and correctly and then a means is established for preventing them to reoccur.

"I also think that this institution is committed to this community and is grateful to it for supporting our presence."

Being a physician, Pennell explained, "gives you a distinctive opportunity to make a difference in the lives of people. Being chief broadens that opportunity for the greater betterment of their care. Our care level could not be as extensive or as stable without the safekeeping nurture provided by CPS's associate and assistant chiefs—and I had the very best.

"We remain a superbly capable, strongly oriented clinical institution that has and continues to keep the patient and the patient's needs first."

To do that, the Medical Center has become acquainted with trying harder, being better, and being chosen.

XVII EPILOGUE: TWICE BLESSED

Today most people begin their lives in hospitals. At birth they receive existence care usually from parents and family. At death they may not have that support system, so they seek the human face of medicine, those medical professionals who sustained them in the between times, be they humble or mighty.

They feel fortunate that in their times of human need they were touched by providers who had found that "faith and knowledge lean largely upon each other in the practice of medicine."[8]

Anyone walking the halls of this Medical Center can see within it the possibilities, responsibilities, hopes, and victories in medicine at this time. These symbols of illness-held-in-abeyance are openly visible, for medicine like faith is built on hope.

People here still try to honor their vows to heal the sick and stand by the lost.

Pennell is an example of this dedication, a man of deeds, not merely words. His postulate is simple: Life has no meaning unless it has responsibilities. Like a father, he nurtures those with whom he walks, cries, laughs, wonders, and heals, be they mighty or humble.

He does not seek gratitude. He feels it is his privilege to recognize and answer the needs of patients, staff, and colleagues and to help them reach their potential in wholeness. He feels reward for servant-leadership is not measured in success, income, positions, possessions, or status. Rather, it is directly related to what one believes or where one puts his or her faith.

Reward, he knows, comes in later life.

This tribute to his loyalty and personage as a doyen and as one of the chiefs is an example of those with multitalented abilities who work and give and keep watch at this Medical Center. Their individual contributions may not be fully realized for some time.

---

[8] Peter Mere Latham (1798-1875) *Collected Works*, Book I.

Pennell's colleagues are grateful for his integrity and willingness to champion their causes. His patients recall his dependability, faithfulness, and presence in times of disrepair. Baptists will come to realize that probably never again will they have a more noble ally or a more gifted spokesman, for he exuberates his Christian goodness and belief in the sanctity and equality of all people.

Here is a man who gave beyond himself. The generosity of his soul and service will be remembered in years to come by those touched by his eminence.

Pennell wanted to bring his medical school and hospital into a more perfect union. He wanted their fusion to be seamless, a merger into a single unified coequal whole: one voice, one commitment, one discipline—a consolidation effort that lost by one vote.

But defeat did not deter Pennell's dream to help this Medical Center become its very best, the chosen, for all who come to its doors in pursuit of restoration.

He cultivated that promise while serving as Chief of Professional Services and he did it during the Medical Center's most turbulent and demanding season.

Earlier on through his faith, Pennell learned that both failure and success can give birth to possibilities, and he realized that "The Miracle on Hawthorne Hill" must be preserved so that those who come to it will continue to be twice blessed.

AFTERWORD

By Len B. Preslar, President and CEO,
The North Carolina Baptist Hospitals, Incorporated

We serve in the present, but we must see that our door to the future remains open because we laid and nurtured a secure foundation for Wake Forest University Baptist Medical Center.

Our future holds great promise—and prompts many questions. The promise of excellence is quite real and being "among the best" quite realizable. Perhaps in many areas we are already among the best, but we know ourselves too well to accept that "we have arrived."

Our quest for excellence must be perpetual, for that is the role of an academic medical center system. Many of the challenges that confront us are a consequence of our own success. In fact, perhaps the potential complacency bred by past successes is one of our greatest barriers to future success. For us, success is defined by excellence, and this will remain our foundation value.

The facilities and services on Hawthorne Hill have grown remarkably during the past two decades. The facility additions now on the drawing board for the core campus fill the Hill to capacity. We have begun to reconsider the highest and best use of some of the oldest facilities on campus. Some, like the South and West Buildings of Baptist Hospital, are likely to remain and be used only for administrative offices. Others, like the Progressive Care facility, may give way to new structures, taking better advantage of the increasingly scarce building sites on the Hill. Second campus alternatives are very real.

But land and facilities aren't the only constraints to developing additional programs and services.

Infrastructure needs, as mundane as parking and elevator services, seem increasingly difficult in the portions required. For an organization committed to service excellence, our size presents an increasing challenge to success, so our upcoming planning cycle will address the question, "If to grow, then where? And what?"

Some believe we should concentrate fully on achieving excellence within our core mission rather than on further growth. Others believe it is virtually impossible to maintain at the status quo: One either grows or one shrinks. The answer, I suspect, lies in between: selectively growing key programs and services at which we truly excel or have the opportunity to excel. The standard for other programs and services will not be on mediocrity but rather excellence at a more moderate size. In this world of limited resources, time, and energy, a focused emphasis will have a much higher probability for success at the highest level.

Such an emphasis is reflected in the excellence of our Emergency Department that records more than 59,000 visits annually. In renewing the Medical Center's Level One Trauma Center designation in 2000, the Trauma Subcommittee of the State Emergency Medical Services Advisory Committee said, "A major strength is the outstanding and long-standing trauma and emergency medicine leadership that has lent continuity to the overall trauma program. Commitment is broad based, from a wide spectrum of the trauma team. In addition, the pediatric trauma service is well developed. There is also an impressive physical plant [and] ... critical care research is outstanding." The primary reviewer for the commission summed it up by saying that the facility overall is "a showcase trauma center for the State of North Carolina."

Parallel emphasis will be given to programs and services in both the clinical and research arenas, enabling a perpetuation of clinical distinctiveness for those programs commanding our major focus. At present, our primary focus will be on cardiovascular, oncology, the neurosciences, age-related programs for the elderly and children, and women's health emphasizing post-childbearing years, and molecular medicine and genetics. These represent the services correlating to the major mortality and morbidity concerns of the population we serve. They also represent areas of service where a highly specialized approach to care is warranted and correlated to excellence.

In all these arenas, our clinical enterprise will continue to treat the most severely ill and injured of the region, complementing the more limited capabilities of the relatively small communities comprising the region. These are the programs and services through which we can have a significant and favorable impact on the health status of the region.

So long as we sustain excellence and distinctiveness in filling this role, we believe our future is secure.

We firmly believe that the hospital's excellence and distinctiveness is furthered by our relationship with the medical school, jointly comprising one of our nation's premier academic medical centers. In recognition of this belief, the executive and governance leadership of our two organizations have solidified and advanced our relationship through a new affiliation agreement and closer linkages of governance.

In recent years, Baptist Hospital has significantly enhanced its financial support of the academic mission. Conversely, the Wake Forest University School of Medicine has made major commitments to a growing research enterprise that promises to further our clinical distinctiveness while advancing the science of medicine on a national level. Our medical staff—from the clinical faculty of the medical school—has committed itself to a broad array of evidence-based medicine initiatives that will further both the effectiveness and efficiency of patient care services throughout the Medical Center.

The care and feeding of the diverse relationships within academic medical centers require considerable energy and time from leadership, but it is time well spent. Our ongoing challenge will be to further our mutual success by cultivating an increasingly collegial and respectful set of relationships throughout our organization.

Our commitment to excellence encompasses not only the science of medicine but also the art of medicine. Our commitment to the art of medicine is founded within our Judeo-Christian heritage, represented by one of our four core values: compassion. It is essential that we minister to the totality of our patients' needs, not only the physical and mental but also the spiritual and emotional.

Our institutional size complicates our commitment to service excellence and to genuine compassionate care, but we are as committed to medicine's art as we are to its science, recognizing both are essential dimensions of excellence.

Our patients and their families often remark, "Even upon entering Baptist Hospital, we recognize that there is something unique about the place, something that feels good and is reassuring." We are determined that this part of our history and culture will be characteristic of our future as well.

Because of future constraints on our Hawthorne Hill campus, we have begun to consider alternative sites for growth. We are asking what role we should play in enabling appropriate community-based health care services in counties other than Forsyth. Our preference is not to duplicate existing community providers but rather to cooperate with and support the independence of these organizations and groups.

Much of our network development strategy centers on supporting these entities and linking with them in ways that facilitate excellence and continuity of care. We also recognize that increasing numbers of these community providers are unstable and vulnerable and several are in communities immediately contiguous to Winston-Salem. So we are asking what role we should play within these communities and whether our presence there would concurrently present a stabilizing force while also furthering our core mission.

Again, because resources are limited, we recognize the need to be cautious, assuring that our response is sustainable over time.

Health care delivery for too long has been fragmented among unrelated providers of care, characterized by discontinuities in diagnosis, treatment, rehabilitation, and health maintenance. There remain opportunities to make our health care delivery system far more system-like.

We believe that a significant part of this effort will be addressed by information technology, founded in an electronic medical record that breaks through the barriers of geographic distance, time, paper, and massive data. At the present time, we are completing a major five-year project culminating in a fully integrated electronic medical record throughout our Medical Center. The potential this asset represents for facilitating excellent and predictable care cannot be overestimated.

We also believe that systems integration among various settings of care represents a significant opportunity to enhance efficiency and effectiveness for improving health status for patients served. So our programs in home health, rehabilitation and subacute care, and long-term care are likely to continue and perhaps grow. Reimbursement for these programs is challenging, most particularly for high-acuity patients, and this characterizes many of the patients being discharged from Baptist Hospital.

Many providers of these services simply will not accept these more challenging patients, necessitating our consideration to offer these ancillary services ourselves. This strategy serves to decompress demand for acute services at Baptist Hospital, allowing more efficient and effective use of our core facility.

What I am describing here might be called a "virtual integrated health care system," where many of the participants involved in caring for the population we serve are independent providers not owned or controlled by our Medical Center. We have shared in caring for this patient population for many years, complementing one another's roles and respecting the role we each play, but we can do a far better job of continuity of care for this patient population.

We also know that earlier detection of disease and lifestyle intervention to prevent disease and injury represents significant opportunities for improving the health status of this population. The latter, particularly, is an effort requiring substantial participation from all elements of local communities. Engaging communities in such efforts will be yet another challenge of health care for future years.

Community service initiatives, which virtually always require institutional financial support, will remain a part of our core mission. While uncompensated care is perhaps the most obvious and substantial financial commitment, many other needs exist.

Too many children underperform in school because of health-related problems, an issue we are addressing through our School Health Alliance. Far too many children and adults receive inadequate dental care, a problem we are addressing through new dental services at our Downtown Health Plaza and with our mobile dental van. Health disparities are statistically evident among population groups of our community and region, a problem we hope to address in focused efforts through our Downtown Health Plaza and in association with the medical school's Division of Public Health Sciences.

Far too much disease is detected in the later stages of development, a problem we are now addressing through our Target Health screening programs and our Best Health educational services at Hanes Mall.

These and other similar services only begin to scratch the surface of need for wellness and prevention programs through which, over time, the health status of our community can be significantly improved.

As payment for health care services are increasingly constrained, there are fewer and fewer dollars available for these community initiatives. The payoff for such initiatives is quite real, but long-term. Our nation's business and political systems seem unduly focused on short-term payback. To the extent our resources allow, we will remain committed to a longer-term perspective.

Our Division of Pastoral Care has evolved an incredible array of very special services in response to the spiritual needs of our patients, as well as to the needs of churches across the state. Numerous studies have now documented what we have known since our founding that a strong personal faith is a powerful tool for healing. As part of the art of medicine, we are determined that God's healing power will be present within Baptist Hospital for all those who will to receive. During the times in which we cannot be as successful as we would wish at healing, His presence would provide solace to both patients and families and to staff.

Through CareNet and our Department of Congregational Health, our Division of Pastoral Care provides counseling services to individuals and churches throughout the state. This is enabled through a creative partnership with local communities, our Baptist State Convention, and with Baptist Hospital. In scope and volume of services, this is easily the most successful network of faith-based counseling services in the country. They are unique and the spoken need for expanding these services is great. We are hopeful that through this creative partnership, we may continue to respond.

Our agenda for the next decade is indeed a full one. It is a challenging and yet noble one.

We envision developing increasingly distinctive and excellent patient care services, promulgating compassionate and patient-centered care, enabling systematically improved care regionally, developing community services that further health status, furthering church-related ministries that offer hope through healing, and being a solid partner with Wake Forest University School of Medicine in advancing the art and science of medicine.

In March 2001, the Institute of Medicine released its report outlining steps for redesigning our nation's health care system. Their report, "Crossing the Quality Chasm: A New Health System for the 21st Century," provides an excellent context for many of our plans. The report urges that all health care organizations adopt as their explicit purpose to continually reduce the burden of illness, injury, and disability and to improve people's health and function. Six major aims were suggested: Health care should be safe, effective, patient-centered, timely, efficient, and equitable. Patient care processes should be redesigned based on best clinical practices. Information technology must be leveraged to improve access to clinical information and to support clinical decision making. Care must be coordinated across patient conditions, services, and settings over time. And both regulatory and reimbursement environments should be examined and revised to remove barriers to quality improvement and to build stronger incentives for enhancing quality and efficiency. The report goes well beyond these observations, but it is fundamentally consistent with our belief that substantial efforts are warranted if our nation's health care system is to be truly excellent and provide value to those it serves.

These are the challenges confronting not only our Medical Center but also our nation's health care system. The rising cost of health care again has begun to accelerate and already exceeds that of any other industrialized nation in terms of both per capita cost and percent of Gross Domestic Product (GDP) going to health care.

Yet for all this investment, our nation's health status indicators are not very good. We can do a better job, but the answers are not simple and are beyond the scope of this book.

Our nation's academic medical centers will play a key role in the future in redefining how care can best be delivered and how health status may be best elevated. Our Medical Center system will be a player in this all-important game of life, as exemplified in the story that unfolds in *Chosen Instrument*.

Indeed, the decades ahead hold not only challenge but also excitement and promise. It will require our very best. Fortunately, many of the best are here. They have chosen to serve and they are instruments of the Great Healer in whose name we serve.

APPENDIXES

APPENDIXES[9]

TABLE OF CONTENTS

[9] Material for the Appendixes was collected from Wake Forest University Baptist Medical Center publications and officials.

BIOGRAPHY

Dr. Timothy Clinard Pennell has given his life to medicine at Wake Forest University Baptist Medical Center, serving as a surgeon, professor of surgical sciences, director of the Office of International Health Affairs (1982-2000), and Chief of Professional Services (1986-2000).

He is a 1955 graduate of Wake Forest University and a 1960 graduate of Bowman Gray School of Medicine, now the Wake Forest University School of Medicine. He received his training in general and cardiothoracic surgery as an intern, resident, and fellow in surgery at The North Carolina Baptist Hospital, Incorporated. He has been an active and leading member of the hospital's medical staff since 1966.

Pennell is a Diplomate of the American Board of Surgery. His professional affiliations include the American College of Surgeons (ACS), American Thoracic Society, Society for Surgery of the Alimentary Tract, and American Medical Association. In 1999, the North Carolina Chapter of ACS presented Pennell with the "Honored Surgeon Award" for his outstanding service and leadership on behalf of all surgeons.

He also is a member and has held offices with the Southern Surgical Association, Southeastern Surgical Congress, North Carolina Medical Society, American College of Physician Executives, North Carolina Surgical Association, Forsyth County Medical Society, and International Digest of Missionary Medicine.

He is the medical school's first director of the Office of International Health Affairs, was the Medical Center's fifth Chief of Professional Services, and is chairman of the House Staff Training Committee for the Department of Surgical Sciences.

He prizes as one of his most beloved honors the recognition given by countless medical students, residents, physician assistants, physicians, colleagues, and missionary professionals who regard him as an honorable teaching surgeon, mentor, and confidant.

In 1996, he received the Distinguished Faculty Award from the Bowman Gray Alumni for his "outstanding service and significant contributions." He also was thanked for his "loyalty and leadership" and for his "tremendous influence and energy" given on behalf of the medical school in the international community as director of International Health Affairs.

He was honored three times by medical students who dedicated their yearbook, *Gray Matter*, to him and who gave him Golden Apple Awards in recognition of his teaching. His medical school colleagues saluted his abilities with Teaching Excellence Awards.

Pennell is the recipient of the Service Medallion from the American College of Surgeons and the Founders Award from the Baptist Medical/Dental Fellowship.

Two grants have been established to honor Pennell. The Pennell-Broyhill International Health Fellowship brings physicians from underdeveloped and nonindustrial countries outside America here for additional medical training. The Timothy Pennell International Scholarship Fund, begun by Pennell's WFUBMC peers, is to provide WFUSM students and spouses the opportunity to experience volunteer medical service in less developed countries, especially in the Third World.

Pennell was born in 1933, the son of the late Madeline White and George C. Pennell of Asheville, N.C. His sister Mary George is married to the Rev. Dr. Luther Brewer.

Pennell married Jacque Clay of Winston-Salem in 1953. They have three children: Melanie, wife of Ed Broyhill II; George Clifton Pennell, husband of Sarah Ruth, all of Winston-Salem; and Jennifer, wife of Ron Gortney, of Fairview, N.C. The Pennells also have 10 grandchildren.

Dr. Pennell and his wife are founding members and teachers at Knollwood Baptist Church in Winston-Salem.

WAKE FOREST UNIVERSITY AND
THE NORTH CAROLINA BAPTIST HOSPITALS,
INCORPORATED

WAKE FOREST UNIVERSITY

Wake Forest Institute was founded in 1834 by the Baptist State Convention of North Carolina on the plantation of Dr. Calvin Jones near the village of Wake Forest, N.C.

Rechartered in 1838 as Wake Forest College, it is one of the oldest institutions of higher learning in the state. It was exclusively a men's college of liberal arts until 1894, when the School of Law was established. Its school of medicine opened in 1902. The college became coeducational in 1942.

In 1956, the college left its 122-year-old campus to Southeastern Baptist Theological Seminary and moved to Winston-Salem to join its medical school on a separate campus. The proposal to relocate the college was offered by the Z. Smith Reynolds Foundation of Winston-Salem and building funds came from the foundation and other sources. Charles H. Babcock and his wife, Mary Reynolds Babcock, donated the site, a part of Reynolda, former estate of Richard J. Reynolds, founder of R. J. Reynolds Tobacco Company, and his wife, Kathryn.

Between 1952 and 1956, the college's first group of 14 Georgian-style building was constructed. The decade that followed became its most expansive, changing the college in size and substance. A stabilizing character was its faculty and staff brought from the old Wake Forest campus. The college began to feel more at home when magnolia trees were planted, students clamored to gain entrance, and growth and development became a constant. To match this progress, the college, after just 11 years on its new campus, was elevated to the status of a university.

Today enrollment stands at more than 6,000. Its School of Business Administration began in 1948 as an undergraduate division and was renamed the Babcock Graduate School of Management in 1969. In 1980, the undergraduate program in business and accountancy was reconstituted as the School of Business and Accountancy and today is the Calloway School of Business and Accountancy. The Division of Graduate Studies, established in 1961, is now organized as the Graduate School of Arts and Sciences, encompassing advanced work in the arts and sciences on both the Hawthorne and Reynolda campuses.

The university has teaching centers at Casa Artom in Venice, at the Worrell House in London, the Flow Haus in Vienna, and other places around the world.

Wake Forest offers courses in more than 40 fields of study leading to the baccalaureate degree. The School of Law offers the Juris Doctor degree, and the Graduate School of Management offers the Master of Business Administration degree. In addition to the Doctor of Medicine degree and training programs for physician assistants, nurse anesthesia, and medical technology, the medical school through the Graduate School offers programs leading to the Master of Science and Doctor of Philosophy degrees in the basic medical sciences. The Graduate School also confers the Master of Arts degree in most areas of the arts and sciences and the Doctor of Philosophy degree in biology, chemistry, and physics.

Through a cooperative program of the Graduate School of Management and the School of Medicine, students can earn both M.D. and M.B.A. degrees. Through a combined program of the Graduate School and the School of Medicine, students can earn both M.D. and Ph.D. degrees.

The university comprises six constituent parts: two undergraduate institutions, Wake Forest College and the Calloway School of Business and Accountancy; the Graduate School of Arts and Sciences; and three professional schools—the School of Law, the

Wake Forest University School of Medicine, and the Babcock Graduate School of Management.

The university's libraries, with a total collection of more than 1.15 million volumes, permits research for undergraduate education in each discipline in which a graduate degree is offered.

Wake Forest has been dedicated to the pursuit of excellence in the liberal arts for 168 years. This means that it believes in education in the fields of human knowledge and achievement as distinguished from education that is technical or narrowly vocational. The college and its graduate schools are defined as singularly focused on learning for its own sake.

A trustee board governs the university and its five schools, assisted by boards of visitors.

In late 2001, the university trustees created a new corporation, Wake Forest University Health Sciences, to provide oversight for its growing medical-related enterprises. The wholly owned, nonprofit, university subsidiary includes Wake Forest University School of Medicine and other operations including co-ownership of Wake Forest University Baptist Behavioral Health (formerly Charter Hospital), and ownership of One Technology Place in downtown Winston-Salem, Amos Cottage and Developmental Evaluation Clinic, and dialysis centers throughout the region.

The corporation is under the leadership of a separate board of directors, elected by university trustees, and its newly named president and CEO, Dr. Richard H. Dean. Dr. Thomas K. Hearn Jr., university president, is a corporation officer and responsible for its working relationship with Wake Forest trustees. While the medical school dean is appointed by Hearn and Dean, he reports to Dean and serves at his pleasure. The medical school faculty continues as part of the university faculty and degrees from all medical school graduates and professional programs continue to be awarded by the university.

The leadership of the university health sciences elects the corporation directors and oversees medical school functions. This includes educating and training over 1,500 students, residents, fellows, and allied health students; preparing a budget now approaching $500 million; managing research enterprises with more than $100 million in annual grants; and supervising over 70 satellite clinics in neighboring communities and states and 767 faculty and over 4,000 other administrative personnel and staff employees.

The university is a member of the Southern Association of Colleges and Schools, the Southern Universities Conference, the Association of American Colleges, and the Council of Graduate Schools in the United States.

WAKE FOREST UNIVERSITY SCHOOL OF MEDICINE

The Wake Forest College Medical School was established in 1902 as a two-year program on the old Wake Forest College campus in Wake Forest. The college leadership felt its addition to the curriculum would bring it national recognition. It began with 13 students and one faculty member, Dr. Fred K. Cooke, a former U.S. Army surgeon who served as its first dean.

The school's initial intent was to "train good physicians." However, its medical students received medical instruction only, for there were no hospital or clinical opportunities available on the campus—except for possible services rendered at the campus infirmary, which became known as "the little North Carolina Baptist Hospital."

Wake Forest operated its fledging medical school as a school of basic sciences—its teachings largely didactic, its laboratories poorly equipped, and its clinical opportunities naught. Students had to go elsewhere to four-year medical schools for proper clinical training and to acquire the M.D. degree.

Despite its meager beginning, the school of medicine was accepted into the membership of the Association of American Medical Colleges in 1904. Four years later, the association listed Wake Forest's medical school as one of 11 requiring two years of pre-medical training before entry into the two-year program.

Despite setbacks caused by the Depression and decisions by the Council on Medical Education of the American Medical Association and the Association of American Medical Colleges to reduce the nation's supply of doctors, Wake Forest and Baptist leaders set out to change this medical school's destiny.

In the mid-to-late 1920s, open discussions were begun by the leadership of the college, medical school, the Baptist State Convention, and North Carolina Baptist Hospital to move the college's medical school to Winston-Salem, linking it with Baptist Hospital, which opened in 1923 under convention guidance.

The proposition seemed the logical way to enlarge the medical program to a four-year school and to add the necessary clinical and laboratory facilities to provide a fully recognized medical degree program.

The college accepted financial support from the Bowman Gray Fund and the Winston-Salem Foundation and the dream of a four-year medical school became a reality. The acquisition of these funds set the medical school on the road toward the accreditation and enlargement it now enjoys as it observes its Centennial anniversary in 2002-2003.

The partnership between Wake Forest and the hospital became official in 1941 when the two joined and became the 69th academic medical center in the nation and the second four-year medical school in North Carolina.

When Wake Forest College moved its medical school to Winston-Salem, it was renamed Bowman Gray School of Medicine in memory of its major new benefactor, the late Bowman Gray, chairman of the board of R. J. Reynolds Tobacco Company. The school located on land donated by hospital trustees. Its first building was the 70,465 square-foot Gray Building, which remains in use today. Then there were 65 full-time faculty members, 42 freshmen, and 30 sophomore medical students. Its initial operating budget was $181,774.

Currently, the student body totals 424, and 259 of them are men, 165 women, and 125 minorities; 540 house officers or residents, 208 graduates, 70 fellows, 92 physician assistants; 16,741 Northwest Area Health Education Center (AHEC) students; 10,950 continuing medical education participants; 53 Pastoral Care; and 1,618 nursing students (in corporation with Forsyth Technical Community College, Winston-Salem State University, University of North Carolina at Greensboro, and Surry, Wilkes, and Caldwell community colleges).

Today the medical school's operating budget is $384,048,000; current direct funding for research and related activites totals over $145 million, received mostly from federal, industry, and state awards; and grants for research and research training total $130.5 million, more than double the amount a decade ago. Tuition for medical students is now $29,640 each for the first and second years. Eighty percent of students now enrolled receive financial assistance.

Wake Forest University School of Medicine today is one of 126 accredited medical schools in the nation, is 36th among American medical schools in total funding from the National Institutes of Health, and is one of the most rapidly growing research enterprises among the top third of American medical schools. Areas of research emphasis include arteriosclerosis, cancer, stroke, hypertension, nutrition, women's health, neurosciences, and aging.

The school has 29 academic departments. There are 767 full-time faculty members, including 538 clinicians, 189 in basic sciences, 40 other faculty (some part-time), and 3,501 administrative and other employees for a total of 6,853 professionals. In addition, 550 physicians from the community are on the part-time clinical faculty.

The university's trustees govern the medical school through their health affairs committee and the senior vice president for health affairs works in close collaboration with and under the authority of the university president.

In 1998, the medical school entered a new curriculum entitled "Prescription for Excellence: A Physician's Pathway to Lifelong Learning." Its goal is to provide graduates with skills to be lifelong learners so that they might stay abreast with the constant advancements in medicine. The program's emphasis includes a broad knowledge of basic clinical science and the ability to analyze and incorporate new knowledge. The new curriculum combines a small-group problem-solving approach, early clinical experiences, and introduction to core biomedical science education and new technology, such as laptop and hand-held computers to access academic and clinical databases. The art of gathering information for improved diagnostic and therapeutic skills leading to medical history-taking is a part of that curriculum as is developing information management skills in electronic resources, communication research, and health cost management. In addition, students are encouraged to adopt attitudes and values that respect life and the desire to serve the suffering, dispensed with integrity and compassion.

This curriculum has become a national model for using informational technology in medical education. For students, the school is a model where care is practiced with visible compassion.

The medical school has seven goals representing the foundation of its undergraduate medical education: self-directed learning and lifelong learning skills, core biomedical science education, clinical skills, problem solving and clinical reasoning skills, interviewing and communication skills, information management skills, and professional attitudes and behavior.

It also provides continuing medical and dental education, as well as leadership and organizational development education and research in continuing medical education.

The Liaison Committee for Medical Education, which accredits American medical schools, in its past two surveys—the last in 2001—named it one of only two medical schools in the nation with no areas of noncompliance.

The interrelatedness between the medical school and hospital allows medical students and house officers opportunity to experience and observe a broad range of unusual medical problems as well as common diseases.

Their education is further enriched through training and practice at Forsyth Medical Center, Forsyth County Health Department, and the Downtown Health Plaza of Baptist Hospital, all in Winston-Salem; Moses Cone Hospital in Greensboro, N.C.; Umstead Hospital in Butner, N.C.; and other clinic sites at cooperating institutions.

The school of medicine has trained thousands of doctors who now practice in Winston-Salem, communities across the state, and across the nation. About a third of its graduates remain in the area for their professional careers.

Its Office of International Health Affairs offers opportunities for overseas study and service to medical students and physicians. It also helps to develop affiliations with medical schools around the world. Currently these partnerships exist in China, Japan, India, Italy, and at other health care institutions.

The medical school's Coy C. Carpenter Library has holdings of more than 145,000 volumes, 3,800 medical and scientific journals, and more than 3,000 audiovisuals. The library offers computer-based online search services to Medical Center personnel and the public. The library's Dorothy Carpenter Medical Archives is the repository and reference center for Medical Center historical records and the official repository for several national professional associations.

The medical school is a member of the Association of American Medical Colleges (AAMC) and is accredited by the Liaison Committee on Medical Education, which is jointly sponsored by the Council on Medical Education of the American Medical Association (AMA) and the AAMC. The biomedical graduate studies program is a unit of the Graduate School of WFU and has the approval of the Southern Association of Colleges and Secondary Schools. The Physician Assistant Program (PAP) is accredited by the AMA's Commission Accreditation of Allied Health Programs (CAAHP).

Long-range plans were announced in August 2002 for the medical school's enlarged presence in Piedmont Triad Research Park in downtown Winston-Salem. The medical school, part of Wake Forest University Health Sciences, is a partner in the future expansion and development of the research park as a major addition to North Carolina's "Biotechnology Corridor." The endorsement by Wake Forest University and its medical school underscores their commitment to the development of the inner city, its economic growth, and its diversification. The medical school is working with officials from the university, city government, and Idealliance, the chief research park developer. Two of the four multistory buildings in the park are owned by the medical school, and it already has its Physician Assistant program and Department of Physiology and Pharmacology located there as well as ongoing clinical research. Expansion to the park gives the university medical school possibility for continued growth and development now that there is no more land available on Hawthorne Hill.

Within the next 10 to 15 years, the park is expected to expand more than 10 times its current five-block area, reaching its neighbors Winston-Salem State University to the east and Salem College and Academy to the south. Currently the park has 19 tenants, about 600 employees, and a gross payroll of $25 million. In maturity, the park could offer employment to another 10,000, provide annual property tax revenues of about $5 million, add over $2.5 billion in total economic benefits, and entice start-up companies in technology and laboratory operations, retail businesses, and restaurants. The research park site was once a manufacturing center for R. J. Reynolds Tobacco Company, which has donated land and buildings to the park.

The medical school's Centennial celebration began in October 2002. Its theme is "The Legacy of Yesterday, the Promise of Tomorrow." The featured speaker at the opening convocation October 10, 2002, in Wait Chapel on the university's Reynolda Campus was Craig Venter, Ph.D., a pioneer scientist in genomics, who spoke on "Sequencing the Human Genome: Gateway to a New Era in Science and Medicine." His topic the next day at the medical center's Bowman Gray campus was "The Genomics Era from Microbes to Man and Beyond." Venter, a former scientist with the federal National Institutes of Health, founded The Institute for Genomic Research (TIGR) in 1992 and Celera Genomics in 1998. In 2002, he started TIGR Center for Advancement of Genomics, a policy institute, and Institute for Biological Energy, which is studying the possibility of genetically engineered microbes to produce energy and to help clean the environment.

Both addresses were part of the medical school's annual alumni weekend. Other events included the unveiling of a statue of Bowman Gray Sr. in recognition of his massive contributions to the medical school's early stability, growth, and educational excellence. This event was held at the renovated and newly named Bowman Gray Alumni Plaza on Hawthorne Road. Earline heath King, Winston-Salem artist, designed the bronze statue of Gray, the man responsible for bringing the medical school to Winston-Salem. Later Dr. Richard Horton, editor of the renown British medical journal *The Lancet*, spoke on "Ethical Conflicts in Medical Publishing."

Other events in the Centennial 2002-2003 observance included a Mini-Medical School on five consecutive Tuesday nights, October 15-November 12, 2002, for the lay public when Medical Center staff discussed five key areas of medical science—genetics, radiology, cancer, cardiology, and physiology and pharmacology. A nine-part series on the history and future of the medical school appeared in *Southern Medical Journal* in its October, November, and December 2002 issues; a collector's reprint will be available in January 2003. *Visions*, a magazine for Wake Forest University Baptist Medical Center alumni, faculty, and friends, will devote its winter issue to the Centennial. Continuing medical education programs, scheduled throughout the year, will feature nationally recognized speakers discussing medical professions in obstetrics/gynecology, diabetes management, neurology, pediatrics, otolaryngology, and surgery. In the spring of 2003, medical school representatives from across the nation will gather at the Medical Center for a presentation on "Academic Computing," the latest uses of technology in medical education.

A hardbound collection of over 400 historical photographs, *One Hundred Years of Medicine: Legacy and Promise*, dating from the early days of the medical school, was published in September. A permanent display of historical photos, architectural models, and early medical artifacts, *The Legacy and Promise*, opened in mid-October in the Nutrition Education Wing of the Nutrition Center.

THE NORTH CAROLINA BAPTIST HOSPITALS, INCORPORATED

The hospital began as a proposal in 1919 by North Carolina Baptists who wanted to extend their statewide ministry to the sick and poor. A year later, the convention selected Winston-Salem and 11.2 acres in the "wilds of Ardmore" for the hospital's site. Construction on its first building, a five-story facility, began in 1921. The hospital opened on May 28, 1923, with 88 beds, 20 bassinets, and a School of Nursing.

In preparation for its 1941 partnership with the medical school, the hospital expanded its capabilities to 270 beds and 50 bassinets. Its operating budget was $225,642 and patients paid $2 per day for room and board. Today the hospital's budget is $477,361,000.

A three-story home for nurses was built in 1928, expanded in 1945, renovated in 1959, and finally transformed into a 79-bed progressive care center for patients. The School of Nursing closed in 1974.

Baptist is the teaching hospital for the Wake Forest University School of Medicine and the Medical Center's primary clinical arm that includes inpatient hospitals, a community health center, a health maintenance organization, and primary care centers. It also is the region's main referral center of tertiary care or the full range of care under one roof of management.

On the staff at the hospital are 1,798 registered nurses, 482 licensed practical nurses and nursing assistants, 934 clinical professions, 537 house officers, and 3,351 administrative and other staff for a total of 6,853 personnel. It has a full-time medical staff of 486 physicians, all of whom are faculty members of Wake Forest University School of Medicine.

Baptist now contains 781 general hospital beds and included within that number are 93 intensive care beds; a 26-bed intermediate care unit; a 16-bed coronary care unit; 138-bed Brenner Children's Hospital and Health Services and its 35-bed intensive care nursery; 57 cancer beds; a 12-bed bone marrow transplant unit; 44 psychiatry beds; a 24-room inpatient operating suite with an adjoining 21-bed postanesthesia unit; a 39-bed rehabilitation unit, a 6-bed burn unit, and 70 short-stay day hospital beds for outpatients.

Annually there are about 31,000 hospital inpatient admissions, nearly 16,000 day hospital stays, 59,098 emergency department outpatient visits, 547,594 other outpatient visits (including Wake Forest University Physicians' clinics and surgery), and 50,806 visits at the Downtown Health Plaza of Baptist Hospital.

During 2001, its main operating room suite completed 18,333 cases requiring 52,649 hours of surgery; and its outpatient surgery center performed 7,366 cases requiring 9,587 hours of surgery. The combined results of these two surgical services resulted in over $142 million in patient billing based on anesthesia, room time, and recovery charges. During the next two years, the hospital will increase its outpatient operating rooms from seven to eight, its inpatient operating rooms to 25, and open a new eight-room pediatric surgery center. In connection with these additions, all three operating room suites will be outfitted with equipment needed for the latest minimally invasive surgery technology.

The hospital's case-severity index is the highest for general hospitals in North Carolina, but its risk-adjust in-hospital mortality rate is well below the expected rate. Average charges for the most frequently treated diagnoses are among the lowest in the state, when adjusted for severity.

Baptist has its own nurse anesthesia and medical technology teaching programs and is the clinical site for eight programs of Forsyth Technical Community College. The nurse anesthesia program was established in 1942 as a hospital-medical school professional school, using the hospital as the major clinical facility. Nine additional sites are now used for clinical experience. This program is the longest existing program in North Carolina. In 1988 the hospital entered into a cooperative effort with the School of Nursing of the University of North Carolina at Greensboro whereby students can complete the Master of Science in Nursing (MSN) degree in anesthesia nursing, a 24-month program.

The hospital's Division of Pastoral Care operates an educational program for clergy and laypersons, works closely with the state's Baptist churches, provides the staff for the CareNet pastoral counseling centers across the state helping churches identify their own goals and objectives, and counsels individual ministers who need support.

The hospital serves patients from all of North Carolina, neighboring states, and across the world, who have adopted its christened byword: *"Take me to Baptist."*

The governing body of the hospital is its board of trustees with the hospital president acting on its behalf in the overall management of the hospital.

WAKE FOREST UNIVERSITY BAPTIST MEDICAL CENTER

Wake Forest University Baptist Medical Center became the overarching institutional name when the medical school entered into partnership with the hospital 61 years ago. Its primary campus is adjacent to Business Interstate 40 in the Ardmore community about five miles from Wake Forest's main campus and within walking distance to Winston-Salem's downtown business section.

The Medical Center's 100 buildings are located on a total of 290 acres at various sites within Forsyth and Davidson Counties, including a 196-acre research farm 10 miles away; a midtown research center; and a community health facility in downtown Winston-Salem.

WFUBMC today is one of the nation's preeminent academic medical centers with an integrated health care system providing specialty and subspecialty care and operating acute care, rehabilitation, and long-term care beds. In addition to inpatient care, it provides many outpatient services and community health and information centers.

The Medical Center has 20 subsidiary or affiliate hospitals and conducts 87 satellite clinics throughout its region. Its continuum of care also includes primary care centers, outpatient rehabilitation, dialysis centers, and a long-term nursing facility.

Its major service area is a 26-county region in northwestern North Carolina and southwestern Virginia; however, its arm of care extends across North Carolina, across nearly three-fourths of the nation, and onto three foreign continents.

Its mission of patient care, education, research, and community services is dispensed by its three major members: Wake Forest University School of Medicine, North Carolina Baptist Hospital, and Wake Forest University Physicians.

Physicians and medical scientists of the Medical Center have become leaders in discovering, testing, and bringing to patients the medicine of tomorrow. And today the Medical Center is in the top third of all academic medical centers nationally in its federally funded research from the National Institutes of Health (NIH), the single most important source of support for biomedical research.

The Medical Center is committed to high standards in every specialty, while the main focus of many of its physicians and scientists is on aging, cancer, cardiovascular disease, molecular medicine, nutrition, neurosciences, pediatrics, rehabilitation, and trauma. Increasingly, the Medical Center is upgrading its specialties by establishing comprehensive centers of incredible note, such as those dealing with cancer, women's health, heart, pain, and substance abuse.

Under a 1997 realignment plan, the name of this medical complex officially became Wake Forest University Baptist Medical Center composed of the Wake Forest University Health Services and North Carolina Baptist Hospital. A combined Medical Center board of directors considers matters of mutual concern.

The medical school, under the realignment plan, became the Wake Forest University School of Medicine on the Bowman Gray campus. The Medical Center is on the main or Hawthorne campus.

Medical school and hospital programs are interwoven to provide medical education, patient care, biomedical research, community services, and rehabilitation of the highest professional level.

This has become a necessity as medicine in this new century faces revolutions within the organization and financing of health care, medical technology, government budget reductions that impact biomedical research and medical education, and increasing patient admissions with multisystem disabilities.

The evolution of the Medical Center has been so remarkable that it has become affectionately known as "The Miracle on Hawthorne Hill." It also has been identified as being there "for my family" and for being there "for my parents, too." Its development has become more intensified over the past 25 years as its three institutions expanded their services and facilities to meet society's changing health care needs.

In 1991 the Medical Center, then in its 50th anniversary year, completed a $200 million building program that doubled its space for research, specialty services, and patient care. Added were a 12-story Clinical Sciences Building, a 15-story North Tower, and a sixth floor to the Hanes Research Building.

In 1992 construction began on another $200 million expansion program adding five buildings. The Nursing Center at Oak Summit, a170-bed facility located in northern Forsyth County, opened in 1993. It includes100 skilled nursing beds, 60 intermediate care beds, and 10-beds for ventilator-dependent patients, one of only four in the state offering this care.

Ardmore Tower East includes three floors of private rooms for patients, expanded operating room facilities, a state-of-the-art Emergency Department, a 35-bed day hospital, Pharmacy Department, and a dietary kitchen and dining area. A 2,234-space parking deck provides surveillance monitoring for Medical Center employees.

Two freestanding units also were added: the J. Paul Sticht Center on Aging and Rehabilitation with 79 beds and various medical services, and CompRehab Plaza, one of the largest outpatient rehabilitation facilities on the East Coast, housing a complete spectrum of physical rehabilitation and related physician and clinical services. The Sticht Center is on the main campus. CompRehab is located across from the Medical Center in a separate complex.

A sixth building, an 11-story Center for Research on Human Nutrition and Chronic Disease Prevention, is still under construction; however, parts are in use.

An 11-story Ardmore Tower West, completed in 2002, includes an entirely new and enlarged Brenner Children's Hospital and Health Services. Its other floors are being used for operating and surgical facilities, outpatient hospital services, and cardiac catheterization labs.

WAKE FOREST UNIVERSITY PHYSICIANS

Wake Forest University Physicians, called WFUP for short, is comprised of over 450 physicians who are the board-certified, or the equivalent, full-time clinical faculty of Wake Forest University School of Medicine.

They also serve as the attending staff of Baptist Hospital. WFUP administers members' outpatient clinics that comprise about 85 medical and surgical specialties.

CURRENT MEDICAL CENTER ADMINISTRATION

—Dr. Richard H. Dean, President and Chief Executive Officer of Wake Forest University Health Sciences and Director of Wake Forest University Baptist Medical Center.

—Len B. Preslar Jr., President and Chief Executive Officer of The North Carolina Baptist Hospitals, Incorporated.

—Dr. William B. Applegate, Senior Vice President of Wake Forest University Health Services and Dean of Wake Forest University School of Medicine.

—Dr. Peter R. Hoffman, Medical Director of Wake Forest University Physicians (WFUP).

—Dr. Vardaman M. Buckalew Jr., Chief of Professional Services.

RECOGNITION RECEIVED IN THIS NEW CENTURY

Each year the Medical Center is the recipient of prestigious awards that set it apart in honored ways. In this new century, the Medical Center continues to be selected for many more remarkable accolades that salute the dedication, sophistication, compassion, and abilities of both the medical school and hospital. For example:

—In its July 2002 issue, *U.S. News and World Report* once again ranked North Carolina Baptist Hospital as one of America's best, especially in six out of the 17 specialty categories judged. Baptist ranked 15th nationally in geriatrics; 23rd in cancer; 23rd in ear, nose, and throat; 24th in urology; 31st in heart and heart surgery; and 43rd in orthopaedics.

The honored facilities were selected from the top 205 medical centers in the nation's pool of 6,045 hospitals, the majority being teaching hospitals. Baptist met all of the stated requirements. Scores along with data on reputation, mortality, and other factors related to patient care, such as nursing and technology, were considered in the ranking system. Baptist Hospital met nearly all of the latest technologies required in the magazine's measurements.

—Patient satisfaction scores at North Carolina Baptist Hospital of Wake Forest University Baptist Medical Center are among the very highest in the nation, according to a 2002 survey by Press Ganey Associates Inc., the health care industry's top satisfaction measurement and improvement firm. Baptist ranked in the top 1 percent of the nation's major health care facilities, which included Yale-New Haven Hospital, Sloan-Kettering Cancer Center, and Emory University Hospital. The ratings are based on information gathered in surveys mailed to patients following discharge. Baptist was one of 5,900 health care facilities reviewed.

—The WFU School of Medicine ranked 35th among American medical schools receiving funding from the federal government's National Institutes of Health (NIH) for the year ending June 30, 2002. Of the $145.6 million total, the federal government financed 78.9 percent, mostly from NIH.

The medical school's Department of Physiology and Pharmacology was the top recipient with nearly $14.7 million. Other top departments included Internal Medicine,

$13.1 million; Pathology (including Comparative Medicine), $8.5 million; Neurology, $6.8 million; and Biochemistry, $6.5 million.

Public Health Services ranked second among 53 similar medical school departments nationally. Physiology and Pharmacology ranked 4th among 100 departments. Other departments in the top 20 were Neurology, 14th; Pathology, 17th; Radiology, 18th; and Family Medicine, 19th.

While NIH is the largest single source of support for the medical school's biomedical research, other support comes from the state and industry; from voluntary health agencies, such as the American Heart Association and the American Cancer Society; from foundations, such as the Robert Wood Johnson Foundation; from pharmaceutical companies; and from other federal agencies, such as the National Science Foundation, Department of Defense, and Department of Agriculture.

—The Medical Center was named one of America's 100 "Most Wired" hospital and health care systems in the nation in the July 2002 issue of *Hospitals & Health Networks*, the journal of the American Hospital Association. This award is based on the magazine's fourth annual survey of the nation's health care systems on their use of Internet technologies to connect with patients, physicians and nurses, payers, health plans, and employees. Being selected illustrates the hospital's persistent efforts to update its technology in order to improve patient care. The 100 Most Wired were chosen from information received from over 300 organizations representing 794 acute care hospitals, based on their voluntary response to an eight-page survey. The magazine's analysis of data revealed that the nation's most wired hospitals enjoy several advantages: better control of expenses, higher productivity, more efficient utilization management, and better credit ratings.

—For the fourth consecutive year, WFUBMC was listed in September 2002 as one of *Piedmont Parent* magazine's "40 Family-Friendly North Carolina Employers." The magazine's editors chose employers that led the way in family friendliness and that help employees to balance the demands of work and family.

—For the third consecutive year, Piedmont Triad consumers in 2002 named Baptist Hospital as their first choice for overall health care services. Awards are based on scores for the best doctors, nurses, image, reputation, and overall quality in the Piedmont Triad. The Consumer Choice Award is conducted by the independent National Research Corporation (NRC), a health care performance measurement organization. The NRC was founded in 1981 to provide the most up-to-date market information to health care organizations. Consumers were surveyed in Greensboro, Winston-Salem, and High Point for their vote on their hospital of choice.

—The Medical Center received the Employer of the Year of Persons with Disabilities Award in May 2002, which is given by the Division of Vocational Rehabilitation Services of the North Carolina Department of Health and Human Services. This award is bestowed to businesses committed to hiring, training, and promoting people with disabilities and to initiating and encouraging work opportunities for people with disabilities.

—The Medical Center received a certificate of excellence in August 2002 from the North Carolina Department of Health and Human Services for exemplary leadership in creating a mother-friendly workplace that supports breastfeeding, one of only 37 businesses in the state receiving the distinction.

—Of the 670 North Carolina physicians included in the publication *The Best Doctors in America* for 2000-2001, 110, or about 16 percent, are faculty members at Wake Forest University Baptist Medical Center. Best Doctors Inc. of Aiken, S.C., compiles the list, now in its 10th year of publication. Each year the company surveys tens of thousands of leading specialists worldwide and asks them what doctors they would go to for treatment in their specialty. Approximately 30,000 physicians in the United States, or about 4 percent of all American doctors, representing over 40 specialties, are included in this list.

—One hundred and fifty-five medical school faculty serve as editors or on editorial boards of 306 journals or publications.

—Sixty medical school faculty serve as president or chair of 75 major professional or scientific societies.

—One hundred and sixteen medical school faculty serve as consultants to NIH and other federal agencies.

—And about 80 medical school faculty annually receive formal awards and/or recognition for excellence in teaching, research, and/or clinical services.

MEDICAL CENTER FIRSTS

1941: School of Medicine creates the first department of medical genetics in the nation.

1957: Medical Center becomes the first in North Carolina to use cobalt to treat cancer patients.

1959: The Department of Clinics incorporates a professional practice plan—the first of its kind in the nation—now renamed Wake Forest University Physicians (WFUP).

1964: Dr. Jesse Meredith, a Medical Center surgeon, performs first hand reimplantation in the nation.

1969: Ultrasound is used to detect prostate cancer, a first in the nation.

1979: Medical school establishes the nation's first toll-free hot line for information about epilepsy.

1981: Brenner Center for Adolescent Medicine opens, first of its kind in the state.

1983: Magnetic resonance imaging (MRI) system installed, first in the state at an academic medical center.

1983: Medical Center is first in the nation to use transcranial Doppler ultrasound to measure atherosclerotic buildup on the walls of the carotid artery and to image the arterial circulation in the brain.

1986: Physicians use lithotripsy to break up common duct gallstones, the first in the nation.

1989: Medical Center surgeons perform the first single-lung transplant in the state.

1990: Cardiologists become first in the state to successfully open a blocked artery using a laser.

1990: WFUBMC is first in the state to have a molecular cytogenetics (cell genetics) laboratory and to use stereotactic radiosurgery to treat tumors and blood vessel abnormalities deep within the brain.

1997: The J. Paul Sticht Center for Aging and Rehabilitation opens the first facility in the world to incorporate geriatric acute care, transitional care, psychiatry, and rehabilitation, all under one roof.

1999: WFUBMC installs the only Gamma Knife in the state.

1999: The Medical Center is the first in the world to report the successful use of magnetic resonance imaging (MRI) to diagnose significant blockages in blood vessels leading to the heart.

1999: BestHealthSM opens the state's first community health resource and education center in Winston-Salem's Hanes Mall.

1999: Wayne VonSeggen, a WFUBMC employee, is the first physician assistant ever elected to the N.C. Medical Board. He later was elected president.

2001: Wake Forest University Baptist Medical Center begins enrolling healthy men age 55 and older in the largest-ever prostate cancer prevention study to determine if selenium and vitamin E prevent prostate cancer.

2001: Physicians at WFUBMC are first in the world to treat a brain tumor patient with the Food and Drug Administration's newly approved GliaSiteᴿ Radiation Therapy System.

2002: Wake Forest University Baptist Medical Center starts the Center for the Study of Pharmacologic Plasticity in the Presence of Pain.

2002: The ALS Center at Wake Forest University Baptist Medical Center is certified as one of 18 prestigious centers in the country carrying for patients with amotrophic lateral sclerosis or Lou Gehrig's disease.

2002: The Wake Forest University Smell and Taste Center opens, one of only three comprehensive centers in the country and the only one in the Southeast.

OTHER HISTORICAL HIGHLIGHTS

1943: The first graduating class of Bowman Gray School of Medicine receives M.D. degrees.

1944: Baptist Hospital adds programs to train dietitians, nurse anesthetists, and X-ray and medical technologists.

1947: Baptist Hospital opens its School of Pastoral Care.

1956: Wake Forest College moves to Winston-Salem, N.C., and to a new campus, part of Reynolda Estate, the former home of the late R. J. Reynolds, founder of R. J. Reynolds Tobacco Company.

1956: The Medical Center's Davis Memorial Chapel built in memory of Annie Pearl Shore Davis and in honor of Egbert L. Davis.

1956: Baptist Hospital furthers its educational role with the development of separate schools in medical technology, cytotechnology, X-ray technology, nurse anesthesia, medical records librarians, practical nursing, and pastoral counseling.

1964: Both the medical school and hospital formally adopt desegregation policies as related to education, employment, and patient care.

1968: Bowman Gray Medical School establishes a Division of Allied Health Sciences and begins its Physician Assistant program.

1974: Bowman Gray/Baptist Hospital Medical Center organization officially adopted.

1975: Reynolds Health Center opens and is staffed by Medical Center faculty.

1977: Obstetrical services in Forsyth County are consolidated with the opening of new facilities at Forsyth Memorial Hospital.

1982: Level One Trauma Center established at the Medical Center.

1983: A program aimed at increasing minority representation in medicine starts at the Bowman Gray Medical School, supported by a $335,000 grant from the Robert Wood Johnson Foundation.

1985: Bowman Gray School of Medicine signs formal affiliation agreement with Zhongshan Medical Center. Zhongshan, now renamed the SunYat-Sen University of Health Sciences, one of the largest medical centers in the People's Republic of China.

1986: Brenner Children's Hospital is established as part of Baptist Hospital through a gift from the Brenner Foundation.

1986: Baptist Hospital establishes AirCare, a helicopter emergency medical service.

1988: Medical school begins academic affiliation with Tokai University of Japan.

1989: Bone marrow transplantation program is established.

1989: Medical Center surgeons perform the first single-lung transplant in North Carolina.

1990: National Cancer Institute designates the Cancer Center of Wake Forest University as a Comprehensive Cancer Center.

1991: Medical Center is named a Claude D. Pepper Older Americans Independence Center.

1997: The hospital and the medical school become Wake Forest University Baptist

Medical Center, and the Bowman Gray School of Medicine is renamed Wake Forest University School of Medicine.

1997: The medical school establishes a Women's Health Center of Excellence, one of 17 centers nationwide designated by the U. S. Public Health Service.

1997: Medical Center opens the J. Paul Sticht Center on Aging and Rehabilitation with assistance by Baptist Hospital.

1998: Medical school institutes innovative new curriculum for its medical students, combining a small-group problem-solving approach, early clinical experience, and new technology.

1999: Construction begun on the Downtown Health Plaza of Baptist Hospital, replacing Reynolds Health Center.

1999: Medical school receives $40.6 million research grant from the National Institute of Diabetes and Digestive and Kidney Disorders, the largest then in the school's history.

1999: Baptist Hospital became the 14th hospital in the country and the first in North Carolina to be named a Magnet Hospital by the American Nurses Credentialing Center.

2000: Baptist Hospital and Wake Forest University School of Medicine purchase the former Charter Behavioral Health System property and establish Wake Forest University Baptist Behavioral Health Incorporated on a campus northwest of the Medical Center.

2000: Medical school announces plans to hire over 60 new faculty members in five research areas and to strengthen its support of other research efforts as part of a $67 million initiative.

2000: Medical school establishes a Center for Human Genomics on campus to facilitate the identification of high-risk genes linked to common diseases, enabling improved treatment of these diseases.

2000: Medical Center establishes a Forensic Nurse Examiner Program within its Emergency Department to treat victims of domestic violence, sexual assault, and child abuse.

2000: The Downtown Health Plaza of Baptist Hospital opens in Winston-Salem, replacing Reynolds Health Center.

2001: Wake Forest University School of Medicine ranks 35th among the national medical schools receiving funding ($90.3 million in fiscal year 2001) from the National Institutes of Health.

2001: Medical Center physicians are the first in the world to treat a recurrent malignant brain tumor patient with the FDA-approved GliaSite[R] Radiation Therapy System (RTS), a balloon catheter procedure combined with surgery.

2001: The Medical Center becomes the home for the national office of the seven-year $100 million Faith in Action program funded by the Robert Wood Johnson Foundation.

2001: Wake Forest University creates a new corporation, Wake Forest University Health Sciences, a wholly owned nonprofit subsidiary that will manage its medical enterprises, including co-ownership of Wake Forest University Baptist Behavioral Health and ownership of One Technology Place, 10 regional dialysis centers, and Amos Cottage and Developmental Evaluation Clinic.

2001: As affirmation of its commitment to research, technology, and community development, Wake Forest University School of Medicine purchases One Technology Place in the Piedmont Triad Research Park in downtown Winston-Salem for $8.5 million. It is home to medical school spin-offs and biotechnological-related companies.

2002: North Carolina Baptist Hospital ranks among the top 43 hospitals in the nation in six of the 17 specialties reviewed by *U.S. News and World Report* in its "America's Best Hospitals" issue of July 22, 2002. Its top specialties are geriatrics, 15th; cancer, 23rd; ear, nose, and throat, 23rd; urology, 24th; heart and heart surgery, 31st; and orthopaedics, 43rd.

2002: North Carolina Baptist Hospital is named among America's very best in patient satisfaction. The hospital was ranked in the top 1 percent of the nation's 5,900 health care facilities by Press Ganey Associates Inc., the industry's top satisfaction measurement and improvement firm. Press Ganey based its scores on replies from patients who were mailed surveys following their discharge from these hospital departments: Emergency, Downtown Health Plaza of Baptist Hospital, Outpatient Surgery, Psychiatry, and Rehabilitation.

2002: Wake Forest University School of Medicine establishes the Maya Angelou Research Center on Minority Health to develop methods for closing the health gap between minorities and the rest of the nation's population.

2002: Wake Forest University School of Medicine ranks 35th among national academic centers receiving direct funding from the National Institutes of Health.

2002: University Dental Associates (UDA) at the Medical Center, founded in 1997, receives full accreditation from the Accreditation Association for Ambulatory Health Care and becomes one of only 12 dental group practices in the United States to have received accreditation status.

2002: Brenner Children's Hospital and Health Services at the Medical Center opens its new and expanded $132 million hospital in Ardmore Tower West.

2002: A $6.1 million research Center for the Study of Pharmacologic Plasticity in the Presence of Pain opens at the Medical Center, funded by a five-year grant from the National Institute for Neurologic Diseases and Stroke of the National Institutes of Health.

2002: North Carolina Baptist Blood Bank is granted accreditation by the American Association of Blood Banks (AABB), becoming one of 2,000 similar facilities in the nation to have earned AABB accreditation.

2002: The Medical Center begins construction on a $75 million Outpatient Comprehensive Cancer Center of Wake Forest University, a consolidation of all its existing outpatient oncology services to one location, with completion expected in 2003.

2002: The world's first live Internet broadcast of a surgical procedure for a deep brain stimulator implantation to control Parkinson's disease takes place on the Medical Center's website.

2002: Wake Forest University and its School of Medicine enlarge their presence in Piedmont Triad Research Park in downtown Winston-Salem. They are partners in the future expansion and development of the park as a major addition to North Carolina's "Biotechnology Corridor." The medical school already has programs in the research park and owns two of its four buildings. The park also offers the university medical school an alternative campus site for its future growth and development now that no more land is available on Hawthorne Hill.

2002: The School of Medicine received a five-year $20 million grant from the National Institute of Diabetes, Digestive, and Kidney Diseases of the National Institutes of Health to coordinate a worldwide effort to identify the genes that determine susceptibility to Type 1 diabetes.

2002: Baptist Hospital received continued accreditation from the Joint Commission on Accreditation of Healthcare Organizations (JCAHO), earning a score of 97, achieved by only 10 percent of hospitals nationwide. The accreditation was awarded with "full standards compliance," the highest level granted by JCAHO and regarded in the industry as the gold seal of approval for meeting stringent standards of performance. The survey is conducted every three years.

2002: Outside support for research and related activities at WFU School of Medicine reached $145.6 million in the year ending June 30, an increase of nearly $13 million or 9.6 percent over the $132.8 million received in the previous year.

2002: Wake Forest University School of Medicine was given a $450,000 grant from the National Heart, Lung, and Blood Institute to fund a community-based education project designed to reduce the incidence of strokes among African Americans.

2002: Faced with a mushrooming caseload, Wake Forest University Health Services is seeking permission from the State of North Carolina to add another three dialysis centers to the 10 it currently operates: three in Forsyth County, two each in Guilford, Surry, and Iredell counties, and one in Davidson County. The certificate of need applications are for new facilities in nearby Thomasville, western Iredell County, and King.

CORE MISSION STATEMENT

The faculty and staff of the medical school and the hospital decided in June 1973 to better serve society by formally stating—and adopting—this Core Mission.

WAKE FOREST UNIVERSITY BAPTIST MEDICAL CENTER, WITHIN THE LIMITS OF ITS RESOURCES, COMMITS ITSELF TO SERVE SOCIETY:

•By providing superior education for students and teachers of medicine and related health professions;

•By rendering a continuum of exemplary and efficient patient care in an environment which emphasizes scholarship and human dignity and principles embodied in the Judeo-Christian traditions;

•By fostering the discovery and application of new knowledge through basic and clinical research in the biomedical and relevant social services; and

•By cooperating within the community, region, and nation through active participation in efforts to improve the health and well-being of the community.

MEDICAL CENTER AFFILIATES

Hospitals affiliated with the Medical Center include Alexander Community, Alleghany Memorial, Angel Community, Ashe Memorial, Blowing Rock, Catawba Memorial, Hugh Chatham Memorial, Lexington Memorial, Morehead Memorial, Northern of Surry County, Rowan Regional Medical Center, Rutherford, Twin County Regional, University of North Carolina Health Plan, Veterans Affairs Medical Center, and Wilkes Regional Medical Center, all of North Carolina. The affiliates in Virginia include R.J. Reynolds-Patrick County Memorial and Memorial of Martinsville and Henry County.

SERVICES CONNECTED TO THE MEDICAL CENTER

—**Aegis Family Health Centers**R were formed in 1994 as a not-for-profit joint venture between Wake Forest University School of Medicine and Baptist Hospital, but the centers are now wholly owned by the hospital. The centers were begun in an effort to stabilize and expand cost-affordable, high-quality primary care services to residents of communities located in the area and throughout Western North Carolina. Aegis has grown from four health care providers in three freestanding locations in two counties to 57 health care providers in 13 practice locations in six Western North Carolina counties.

—**Amos Cottage and Developmental Evaluation Clinic** are the sites of the Department of Pediatrics' major emphasis on developmental and behavioral medicine. The clinic assesses the needs of children with developmental disabilities and, in cooperation with the parents or alternate caregivers, formulates a specific therapeutic plan for each patient. In the spring of 2002, the rehabilitation clinic moved to the main campus, where it continues outpatient services, including assessment of orthopaedic, physical and occupational therapy, aqnd speech pathology. Fourth-year medical students electing pediatrics can rotate through these units for exposure to a multidisciplinary and interdisciplinary team approach in the evaluation and treatment of children with developmental disabilities. Pediatric department residents also receive training in developmental medicine through these units.

   —**Baptist Hospital HomeCare** is a not-for-profit medical care provider owned by the hospital and located in South Park Shopping Center. As a certified home health agency, it offers a full range of home care services, including equipment sales, skilled nursing, physical and occupational therapy, medical social work, home health aides, personnel response, long-term care pharmacy, and intravenous drug therapy for patients in their own homes

   —**Brenner Children's Hospital and Health Services** treats patients from birth to age 21 from Western North Carolina as well as parts of Virginia, South Carolina, and Tennessee. It also includes the Brenner Center for Adolescent Medicine, one of about 27 such centers in the nation. Brenner Children's Hospital supports research, community service, and education on a wide variety of health issues affecting children and adolescents and provides the care and training necessary to manage their health issues. Currently the center's projects involve collaborations among the Departments of Pediatrics, Public Health Sciences, Psychiatry, Sociology, Psychology, and Communication. Community collaborations include the Winston-Salem/Forsyth County Schools, Forsyth County Juvenile Justice Council, Winston-Salem Police Department, U.S. Attorney's Office, Adolescent Pregnancy Prevention Coalition of North Carolina, and Governor's Institute on Drug and Alcohol Abuse. Brenner Children's Hospital was established in 1986 to serve critically ill patients and those with complex and serious medical problems. Over 4,500 children are admitted yearly to Brenner Children's Hospital for its full continuum of care including a pediatric emergency room and pediatric and neonatal intensive care units. Its new hospital, located on six of the 11-story Ardmore Tower West—plus a rooftop garden—opened in April 2002. It allows Brenner Children's Hospital to offer patient-friendly services, such as single-occupancy rooms for pediatric patients and their families. The tower's other floors will house operating and surgical areas, outpatient hospital services, and cardiac catherization labs.

   —**CareNet** is a network of pastoral counseling centers across North Carolina offered by Baptist Hospital's Division of Pastoral Care. This is the division's most extensive outreach effort offering holistic treatment that integrates spirituality into the healing process. Therapy is offered for problems such as stress, eating disorders, marriage difficulties, grief, and depression. The pastoral counselors serving these centers are trained in both psychology and theology. Their service is not just for people of faith but for anyone seeking counseling with the added dimension of spiritual values and belief. This is just one area of service provided by the hospital's Division of Pastoral Care. The hospital's concern for this ministry began with the School of Pastoral Care founded in 1947 by Dr. Richard K. Young. The school's focus then was to provide education, training, and ministries to hurting humanity within the hospital and out in the community. The school is one of four emphases of the hospital's mission to provide ministries of growth, hope, and healing in the spirit of Christ through clinical pastoral education programs and faith-based pastoral counseling now in 20 locations across the state, in 14 other states, and in several foreign countries. Its Department of Church and Community Relations is a liaison between the Medical Center and Baptists of North Carolina, as well as other denominations, raising awareness of Medical Center services available to help needy patients with money for medications, food, travel home, and assistance in paying their hospital bill. The Department of Chaplaincy and Pastoral Education provides clinical pastoral counseling education and training—one of the nation's largest—to 70 students annually, and it serves patients and Medical Center employees in pastoral counseling crisis ministry. CareNet is an outgrowth of pastoral care ministry on a statewide basis. It is the nation's largest (21 locations in the state) and highest volume (27,000 clinic visits annually) hospital-based pastoral counseling system. The Department of the Center for Congregational Health reflects the school's commitment to assisting congregations with issues such as conflict and the clarifying of core values.

—**CompRehab** is one of the largest freestanding comprehensive outpatient rehabilitation centers in the nation. It provides rehabilitative care for post-injury, post-operative, and chronic patients. The center encompasses related physician and clinical services, including the Foot and Ankle Center, the Hand Center, the Musculoskeletal Therapy Center, the Neurorehabilitation Center, and the Sports Medicine Center. The center allows patients to see their physicians and therapists on the same visit and at the same location. Its Spine Center offers comprehensive services for back and neck pain, and its Self-Care Spine Program is an educational and therapy program for people with acute spine injury. CompRehab also has a program to familiarize people with devices that facilitate everyday activities, occupational medicine, a clinic for fitting wheelchairs, and a program to evaluate and improve driving skills for people with disabilities.

—**The Dialysis Center of Wake Forest University** operates three programs in Forsyth County, two each in Guilford, Surry, and Iredell counties, and one in Davidson County. The medical school also provides medical coverage for patients in the dialysis unit in North Wilkesboro, owned by Wilkes Regional Medical Center. Wake Forest University Health Services has applied to the State of North Carolina for certificates of need to open and operate additional dialysis centers in Thomasville, western Iredell County, and King, due to a rapidly increasing caseload of people suffering from chronic kidney failure, particularly African Americans. Some of the patients are treated at home, using a different method of dialysis. The centers also are used for research, including clinical trials financed both by NIH and private industry, and for training physicians on nephrology fellowships. The centers are supervised by physicians from the medical school's Section on Nephrology of the Department of Internal Medicine.

—**Faith in Action** has located its national program office at the Medical Center. This is a new seven-year $100 million health care support program funded by the Robert Wood Johnson Foundation. Its staff is identifying and approving interfaith organizations across the country for foundation grants. The grants of $35,000 each are being used to start volunteer-based support systems for the frail elderly, disabled, and chronically ill. The program will fund about 2,000 sites over the seven years. Grants will pay for coordinators to recruit and train volunteers to assist home- or institution-bound patients with basic needs such as transportation, shopping, errands, and companionship. It is known that over 10 million Americans are isolated and in need of this kind of personal health care. The program also will provide respite assistance for family caregivers. The Robert Wood Johnson Foundation is the nation's largest foundation devoted to improving the health and health care of all Americans.

—**Forsyth County Carolina Access** is a joint endeavor with the hospital and medical school to administer the Carolina Access II program for Carolina Access Medicaid patients in Forsyth County.

—The medical school is affiliated with the **W.G. (Bill) Hefner Salisbury Veterans Affairs Medical Center,** located in Salisbury, N.C., which is about 50 miles from Winston-Salem. This V.A. Medical Center is a 533-bed general medical, surgical, and mental health facility serving over 29,000 veterans in the Piedmont Triad area of North Carolina. The Medical Center also provides a full range of outpatient health care in Salisbury, Winston-Salem, and the community-based outpatient clinic in Charlotte, N.C.

—**Hawthorne Inn and Conference Center,** a hospital-owned facility, includes a hotel, conference center, and restaurant for Medical Center use and is open for public meetings. It is located near the Medical Center and Business I-40. Attached to the Baptist Hospital center is **Friendship Place** for people undergoing daily outpatient treatment. Some people live too far away to take multiple days of treatments or blood products and their insurance company may not authorize further hospital days. Users must meet specific criteria, which include the need for a minimum of three days of daily treatment, a travel distance greater than 50 miles, and the ability to function mostly independently with basic care needs. Friendship Place opened in January 1997 with 10 rooms, two furnished kitchens, a living room or group meeting area, and a reading and game room. Patients can use a shuttle service to the Medical Center. They have access to the hotel's fitness center, swimming pool, and coin-operated laundry.

—**Home Care of Western Carolina Inc.**, a for-profit subsidiary of Baptist Hospital, provides infusion equipment and handles a limited amount of durable medical equipment. It is located at 3187 Peters Creek Parkway in Winston-Salem.

—**Hoots Memorial Hospital,** a 46-bed medical and surgical hospital in Yadkinville, N.C., is leased by Baptist Hospital. Hoots also includes the 24-bed Yadkin Heritage Extended Care Facility. The hospital provides basic ancillary, emergency department, and inpatient services typical of a critical access hospital. An Aegis medical practice is located on its campus.

—**MedCost** is a managed care company owned jointly by Baptist Hospital and Carolinas HealthCare Systems of Charlotte. It is the largest preferred provider organizational network in the Carolinas.

—**The Nursing Center at Oak Summit** was opened in July 1993 by Baptist Hospital. The 170-bed facility includes 100 skilled nursing beds, 60 intermediate care beds, and a 10-bed unit for ventilator-dependent patients. It is one of only four nursing centers in the state offering care for ventilator-dependent patients.

—The medical school opened its second building in the **Piedmont Triad Research Park** in downtown Winston-Salem in 2001. It is located on a site formerly occupied by tobacco factories destroyed by fire in 1998. Acquired from R. J. Reynolds Tobacco Company, the site in Albert Hall is home to medical school related programs, including the physician assistant program (now offering a master's degree-granting program), teaching laboratories, and academic and administrative offices. The first unit houses the medical school's Department of Physiology and Pharmacology as well as Winston-Salem State University laboratories.

—The Medical Center owns **Piedmont Plaza**, former headquarters of Piedmont Airlines and a former R. J. Reynolds Tobacco Company research building, and **Piedmont Plaza II**, a former office building located a few blocks from the Medical Center. Plaza II has been renovated to house the medical school's Department of Public Health Services and the Women's Health Center. It has shuttle service to the nearby Medical Center complex.

—**Stokes-Reynolds Memorial Hospital,** a general medical and surgical hospital with 53 acute-care beds and 40 long-term care beds located in Danbury, N.C., is leased by Baptist Hospital. The Stokes County hospital operates an outpatient surgical facility in King, N.C., the largest population base in the county. A certificate of need application will soon be filed with the state of North Carolina to build a replacement hospital in King, consisting of 34 acute care beds, and all necessary ancillary support to be owned by and carry the name of Baptist Hospital.

—**Triad Radiographic Imaging** specializes in the repair, maintenance, refurbishment, and resale of radiographic equipment, and it sells a variety of radiology supplies. Its primary customers are small hospitals and physician offices. The company, owned by Baptist Hospital, has been a great benefit to many components of the Medical Center system in providing cost-effective radiographic equipment, film, and other supply items.

—**Wake Forest University Baptist Behavioral Health** is a not-for-profit corporation co-owned by the hospital and medical school. WFUBBH purchased the former Charter Hospital property located on Old Vineyard Road in Winston-Salem in September 2000. After extensive renovations to the three buildings on the campus, the administrative operations began and the first program was initiated in April 2001. That program is a residential treatment center for sexually aggressive children and adolescents. It now has a capacity for 21 beds for adolescents, 12 beds for adolescents with special needs, and 12 beds for children. To meet the educational needs of these young people, the corporation was licensed to open the private Vineyard School. In March 2002, an adolescent day treatment and partial hospitalization program, Journeys, was opened with a capacity to serve 16 children or adolescents. This program serves clients and families previously in Charter's Youth Transitions program, which closed in March 2002. A 20-bed residential program for older adults with substance abuse opened in June 2002.

—The Wake Forest University Laser Center opened in the summer of 2001 with state-of-the-art lasers for a variety of clinical applications operated by the Department of Plastic and Reconstructive Surgery. The center has three new lasers, which have specific use. Treatment is available for removing wrinkles around the eyes, forehead, and mouth; tightening skin on the entire face; treatment for spider and varicose veins; removing facial hair and tattoos; treating vascular lesions; or taking the discoloration out of scars.

MEDICAL RESEARCH CENTERS

Wake Forest University School of Medicine now ranks 35th in the nation among medical schools receiving research money from the National Institutes of Health, the single most important source of support for biomedical research and the largest single source of funds for medical research at WFUSM. The medical school received $90.3 million in fiscal year 2001, up from $72.5 million in 2000. Of the 2002 total of $145.6 million, 78.9 percent came from NIH funds, 10.8 percent from industry, and 8.1 percent from foundations and voluntary health agencies. Most outside support went for research and the rest for projects, such as patient care for people with sickle cell disease or hemophelia, the Child Guidance Clinic, and outreach educational programs.

Its major centers of research include:

—The ALS Center at Wake Forest University Baptist Medical Center today is one of 17 prestigious centers in the country now certified by the ALS National Association. It is recognized for its excellence in the care and treatment of patients with amotrophic lateral sclerosis, better known at Lou Gehrig's disease. The center treats over 100 ALS patients from across the country who seek out the center's ALS neurologists specializing in the fatal, neurodegenerative disease that occurs when motor nerve cells cease functioning and die. In most cases, the patient's mind remains alert but muscle control is completely lost.

—The Center for Human Genomics, established in 2000, is identifying high-risk genes linked to common diseases and their improved treatment. The genomic research encompasses nearly every major research effort at the Medical Center: heart disease, cancer, diabetes, high blood pressure, pulmonary diseases, drug abuse, alcohol abuse, women's health, and aging. The multidisciplinary and multidepartmental center enlarged its faculty as part of the medical school's $67 million research initiative into human genomics. The center's three divisions work closely to examine common complex diseases with a genetic component. The center has five program focuses, two of which already are well established: gene discovery—the genetic basis of diabetes, kidney disease, cardiovascular disease, and cancer; and population informatics—and genetic and molecular epidemiology. The center provides support for three developing programs: functional genomics, which includes developing drugs; translational genomics, which is understanding the function of human genes through use of animal models and developing methods of gene therapy; and clinical translation, which is putting gene discoveries into clinical practice and disease prevention.

—The Center for Investigative Neuroscience is dedicated to research into the treatment of diseases of the central nervous system, which is done in collaboration with over 100 neuroscientists at the university. Its current areas of research include developmental neurobiology, substance abuse, stroke and cerebrovascular diseases, sensory and intersensory function, brain plasticity, neuroimaging, epilepsy, aging, biological psychiatry, computational neuroscience, and the neural bases of behavior, learning, and memory.

—The **Center for Medical Ultrasound** has been involved for over a quarter of a century in ultrasound education and clinical care as well as research into the development of new ultrasound devices. The center coordinates the activities of 18 departments involved in diagnostic ultrasound. It annually performs over 30,000 clinical examinations.

—The **Center for Neurobehavioral Study of Alcohol (CNSA)** is one of 15 alcohol research centers funded by the National Institute on Alcohol Abuse and Alcoholism. Research projects range from studies of alcohol's effects on liver function to brain mechanisms involved in the control of consumption. Many of the center's projects integrate with additional ongoing projects funded from federal and private sources in a unified attempt to understand the mechanisms that control alcohol consumption.

—The **Center for the Neurobiological Investigation of Drug Abuse** is a multidisciplinary research and training center funded by the National Institute on Drug Abuse (NIDA). Major research efforts are examining the brain processes that mediate compulsive cocaine and opiate abuse and another focuses on the development of medications for the treatment of drug abuse that involves a novel chemical approach developed at the university. Its medications development group is active in discovering compounds for future clinical use. The center provides an environment for scientific interactions among faculty and students at the medical school and provides information about substance abuse to the general public through its outreach program. The center's premise is that more effective treatment and prevention of substance abuse can be accomplished through increased knowledge of fundamental biological mechanisms underlying compulsive drug use. The center was established for investigating drug-seeking behavior, particularly in light of the national drug problem.

—Over the next five years, the **Center for the Study of Pharmacologic Plasticity in the Presence of Pain** will study persistent nerve-injury pain and investigate how changes in the nervous system, specifically in the spinal cord, occur in the presence of certain medicines used for pain discomfort. The $6.1 million research center at WFUBMC is being funded by a grant from the National Institute for Neurologic Diseases and Stroke of the National Institutes of Health. This is the second center in the nation funded by the institute. The research will be done both in the laboratory and clinic. Scientists now believe that nerve activity in the spinal cord has a major influence over the perception of pain from damaged nerve endings. Researchers will study the use of a blood pressure medicine called clonidine for chronic pain relief, whether other pain medicines can stop or reverse changes in the nervous system, determine what parts of the brain are affected by the use of heroin for pain, and why certain pain-relieving drugs, such as metanicotine, are more potent in women than men. Wake Forest University School of Medicine and Dr. James C. Eisenach, principal investigator in the new pain center, have patented this drug. It is being manufactured in Winston-Salem by Targacept Inc. The center's goal is to better understand how to treat people with chronic pain. Information learned will be applied to patients in clinical trials through the Piedmont Pain Control Center. Patients will be recruited from a three-state area. The studies will concentrate on patients with lingering pain from back surgeries, industrial injuries that damage a nerve, diabetic neuropathies, shingles pain, and possibly some residual cancer-related pain in people now disease free.

—The **Center for Research on Human Nutrition and Chronic Disease Prevention** is pioneering research into the role diet and nutrition play in the causes, prevention, and treatment of chronic diseases, particularly heart disease, cancer, osteoporosis, and obesity. Its goal is to reduce human suffering and the economic costs of these diseases. Its new $58 million 11-story center, parts of which are still under construction,

184

houses basic science laboratories, human metabolic laboratories, and population research facilities. Its latest $691,000 grant from the U.S. Department of Housing and Urban Development was used to purchase major equipment for its research laboratories into cancer biology, radiation oncology, and cell and gene therapy. This grant brings the federal appropriation total to $20.8 million for the center.

—The Center for Voice Disorders (CVD) is one of the first multidisciplinary voice centers in the nation. It is part of the medical school's Department of Otolaryngology. Its purpose is to foster research and educational programs related to the voice as well as to provide medical services for people with voice problems and other disorders of the larynx or voice box. Currently the center receives about 5,000 patient visits annually. Specialized clinical services are available for people with vocal misuse and overuse syndromes, recurrent laryngitis, spasmodic dysphonia, vocal cord paralysis, aging voice, cancer of the vocal cords, scarred vocal cords, and benign vocal cord growths, such as modules, cysts, granulomas, webs, papillomas, and polyps.

—The Cerebrovascular Research Center is an international leader in the field of stroke research, prevention and treatment of strokes and transient ischemic attacks (TIAs). Two major areas of basic research deal with the clinical management, including diagnosis treatment, rehabilitation, and long-term follow-up of these two diseases and basic research in brain blood circulation and how it is affected by disease and the effects of therapeutic drugs or interventions. It is the headquarters for a major national study testing whether vitamins can prevent the recurrence of stroke.

—The Comparative Medicine Clinical Research Center, begun in 1989, conducts research on animal patients, particularly nonhuman primates, to gain insight into human health and disease. The center's faculty focuses on diseases of human beings with particular public health significance, particularly the prevention of three health problems of aging women: coronary heart disease (especially atherosclerosis), osteoporosis, and cognitive dysfunction (such as Alzheimer's disease). Research grants from the National Institutes of Health (NIH) and others from the private sector support the center's programs. Training opportunities at both the predoctoral and postdoctoral levels are available. The center is located on a 190-acre facility in a nearby rural setting.

—The Comprehensive Cancer Center of Wake Forest University is a driving force in the rapid and sustained growth of cancer programs within the institution. The institution has a strong cancer-funding base with 37 peer-reviewed grants and contracts from the National Cancer Institute (NCI) and nearly an equal number of cancer-focused grants from the National Institutes of Health (NIH), the American Cancer Society, and the U.S. Department of Defense. The center conducts biomedical research at the basic, clinical, and population study levels across five states, offering participation in clinical trials to cancer patients. The center includes over 100 faculty with programs in breast, prostate/genitourinary, lung, gastrointestinal, oral/head and neck, neuro-oncology, and leukemia/ lymphoma. The center's focus currently is set on four programmatic themes: cell growth and survival, DNA damage and cellular defense, clinical research, and cancer control.

—The Comprehensive Epilepsy Center was begun in 1976 with the University of Virginia as a collaborative effort for research in epilepsy. The center currently is involved in research and education that has received international recognition for its contributions to improved patient care. Its objective is to maximize the potential of individuals with epilepsy through research, education, and clinical services. It offers the latest drug therapies for epilepsy and the latest surgery for certain patients whose seizures cannot be controlled with medications. Its six-bed Epilepsy Monitoring Unit uses the latest diagnostic procedures to evaluate patients' suitability for surgery, which results in about 70 percent of patients being seizure-free afterward. It operates a toll-free Epilepsy Information Service that provides information and referral assistance to professionals, their families, and the public: 1-800-642-0500.

—The **Roena Bullis Kulynych Dementia Research Center** opened at the Medical Center in early August 2001 with a $1.2 million gift—and a pledge for an additional $2.5 million—by Petro Kulynych in honor of his late wife Roena, who suffered from dementia. The center researches memory problems and dementia and looks at the influence diseases such as heart, infections, nutrition, and exercise have on memory.

—The **Department of Pediatrics** investigates both clinical and social conditions affecting children ages birth to 18. Current research includes ways to prevent teenage health-risk behaviors, such as underage drinking, smoking, risky sexual behaviors, and violence to resolve conflict. Clinically, researchers are seeking novel treatments for asthma, cystic fibrosis, and heart anomalies.

—The **Diabetes Care Center at Wake Forest University School of Medicine**, begun in 1998, operates the Diabetes Disease Management Program for its patients, teaching them the skills, assistance, and knowledge needed to participate in their self-management of diabetes care. The program emphasizes a multidisciplinary team approach. It also offers a comprehensive approach to support the medical management of the population with diabetes. The program utilizes resources such as case management, diabetes-specific tracking, patient self-management education, and physician/provider education. Collectively these services function to enhance the quality of diabetes care while decreasing health care costs. The medical school has been awarded a five-year $20 million grant by the National Institute of Diabetes, Digestive, and Kidney Diseases of the National Institutes of Health to coordinate a worldwide effort to identify the genes that determine susceptibility to Type 1 diabetes, formally known as insulin-dependent diabetes or juvenile diabetes. The project is called the International Type I Diabetes Genetics Consortium. It has three goals: to establish a new and worldwide collection of 2,500 families with at least two children affected by Type I diabetes, organize the already collected detailed genetic analyses of about 1,800 families, and provide resources. Researchers then can coordinate their efforts to identify the genes that interact to define the risk for Type 1 diabetes. A steering committee from the medical school will coordinate findings from the genetics study, working closely with the Diabetes Institute, the Juvenile Diabetes Research Foundation, the National Institute of Allergy and Infectious Diseases, the National Human Genome Research Institute, and other organizations. Type 1 diabetes occurs when the body's immune system malfunctions, producing an autoimmune response that destroys the insulin-producing beta cells in the pancreas, disallowing the pancreas to produce insulin naturally. Type 1 diabetics need daily insulin injections to stay alive.

—The **General Clinical Research Center (GCRC)** has as its primary mission to provide research with human subjects for their improved care. It is one of 76 such centers located in American academic medical centers funded by NIH. Its operations are a collaborative effort between the medical school and hospital. The center opened in 1993. Its 200 diverse studies include research on women's health, cardiovascular diseases and atherosclerosis, endocrinology, gerontology, infectious diseases and AIDS, inflammation, nephrology, neurology, nutrition and disease, oncology, anesthesiology, pediatrics, and psychiatry. The center has approximately 5,000 research visits per year. Thousands of area residents have participated in its clinical trials or population studies. In 2001, the center was awarded $14.7 million to continue its research for another five years. The grant from NIH's National Center for Research Resources was up over the $9.9 million grant for the past five year's research. This latest grant will be used to pay for specialized facilities and staff and support to continue and strengthen as many as 90 clinical research studies for medical advancements. The funds permitted the creation of a molecular genetics core laboratory and a research affiliation with the Downtown Health Plaza of Baptist Hospital as well as establishing an outpatient pediatric general clinical research center in the new and expanded Brenner Children's Hospital.

—The **Hypertension and Vascular Disease Center** was established in 1992 to amalgamate various efforts in the investigation of the fundamental mechanisms of high blood pressure and vascular disease. The center explores the causes of high blood pressure and related diseases of the heart and blood vessels through investigation of the genetic and molecular mechanisms of hypertension in the setting of clinical research and patient care. Insights gained are translated into approaches that address aspects of secondary and primary prevention of cardiovascular diseases through community-based awareness programs conducted by faculty and applied in graduate medical educational activities.

—The **J. Paul Sticht Center on Aging and Rehabilitation** is a comprehensive effort to learn more about aging, to teach others what is learned, and to improve the health and independence of older people. The center's research is funded by numerous grants from industry and NIH. The heart of the research effort is the Claude D. Pepper Older Americans Independence Center grant, one of the first three named by the National Institute on Aging. The center's research is focused on preventing disability and maintaining the independence of older adults with chronic diseases, such as osteoarthritis, congestive heart failure, and lung disease. Over 30 scientists participate in the center's research program. In addition to training medical students, residents, and fellows in geriatrics, the center also provides continuing education for health professionals through its Appalachian Geriatric Education Center. Sticht is the only facility of its kind offering outpatient care, acute and subacute care, rehabilitation, and psychiatric care for the elderly under one roof. A geriatric day hospital is planned.

—**MICROMED: Resource Center for Intermediate Voltage Electron Microscopy** is a full-service microscopy laboratory that provides instrumentation, technical services, and collaborative support in biomedical research. The facility houses light and electron microscopes and a laser scanning confocal microscope whose use is designed to provide new information related to the structure and chemistry of solid state and biological materials. The resource, established through a partnership involving NIH, the North Carolina Biotechnology Center, and the school of medicine, provides ultrastructural technology to the research community. The laboratory is particularly dedicated to facilitating application of intermediate voltage micoscopy to the ultrastructural research needs of investigators of all disciplines. The resource center contains a Philips CM-30 intermediate voltage electron microscope, a laser scanning confocal microscope, and other instrumentation for standard transmission and scanning electron microscopy.

—**The Positron Emission Tomography Center (PET)** is a facility jointly supported by the medical school and hospital. It opened in 1992 and is considered one of the finest advanced technology facilities of its kind in the world. The center includes advanced instrumentation for imaging and quantifying the distribution of radioactive drugs in the body. The equipment includes PET scanners and extensive computer resources for image processing, analysis, and display and merging PET data with information from other techniques, such as computed tomography (CT) and magnetic resonance imaging (MRI). The center also provides positron-emitting isotopes and a variety of metabolic and physiologic tracer drugs. It recently added a GE Advance™ PET scanner, newest in the state since 1993. It is simpler to use, faster, and produces exceptional whole-body images, especially in detecting cancer stages and determining noninvasively if the cancers are benign or malignant lesions. It also is useful clinically in evaluating patients with epilepsy and determining myocardial viability. The center provides a variety of clinical services, including cancer, brain, and cardiac studies. The center's also serves as a Medical Center faculty research resource.

—Wake Forest University School of Medicine has purchased **One Technology Place** located in downtown Winston-Salem in the Piedmont Triad Community Research Park (PTCRP). The $8.5 million four-story facility confirms the medical school's increasing commitment to work with the city in the development of an economy based on research and technology, particularly biotechnology. Projects that originated at the medical school have already moved to the research park's facilities, including the spin-off companies of **Amplistar, Pilot Therapeutics, PointDx, Prosperon Pharmaceuticals,** and **Kucera Pharmaceuticals.** Amplistar is developing biomarkers for early cancer detection; Pilot is developing evidence-based dietary supplements; PointDx aims to revolutionize how 350 million radiology exams are reported each year; Prosperon is creating compounds to safely treat stroke, spinal cord, and traumatic brain injuries; and Kucera is developing compounds to use with existing drugs to better treat cancers and viruses such as AIDS. The medical school's Department of Physiology and Pharmacology occupies research laboratories in PTCRC. And the school's physician assistant program is located in nearby Albert Hall. Currently One Technology Place has 17 life science, information technology, and business service tenants. One of its newest is **Targacept**, now a privately held research and development pharmaceutical company founded by R. J. Reynolds Tobacco Company in 1997. Targacept leases the top two floors for its corporate headquarters and laboratory facilities. Targacept specializes in the research and development of drugs to treat diseases affecting the nervous system. It currently has products in development for treating Alzheimer's and Parkinson's diseases, ulcerative colitis, depression, pain, and attention deficit disorders.

—**The Substance Abuse Policy Research Program** at Wake Forest University School of Medicine has been awarded a $749,968 grant by the Robert Wood Johnson Foundation for continued national direction of the foundation's substance abuse policy research program. The 10-year research program is in Round VI of grants aimed at producing information on ways to reduce the harm caused by the use of tobacco, alcohol, and illicit drugs. Substance abuse, the nation's top public health problem, is responsible annually for 500,000 preventable deaths.

—**The Wake Forest University Smell and Taste Center** brings together physicians and researchers dedicated to the diagnosis and treatment of patients from across the country who have smell and taste disorders. It is one of only three such comprehensive centers in the nation and the only one in the Southeast. Chronic smell and taste disorders affect about 7 percent of the population, especially the elderly who suffer, as the result, from food choices and intake. This can be detrimental to patients with diabetes and hypertension as well as to cancer patients undergoing chemotherapy or irradiation who either temporarily or permanently lose their sense of taste and cannot eat enough to keep up their weight and strength.

—**The Women's Health Center of Excellence** is one of only 15 national centers of excellence in the nation for women's health designated by the U.S. Public Health Service. It serves as a national model to determine the best means of providing clinic care and health education to women, improving the education of health care providers, conducting state-of-the-art research on the diseases that affect women, and promoting leadership opportunities for women researchers and physicians.

BOOKS ABOUT WAKE FOREST UNIVERSITY BAPTIST MEDICAL CENTER

—*The Story of Medicine at Wake Forest* by Dr. Coy C. Carpenter, the first dean of the medical school after it moved to Winston-Salem to affiliate with The North Carolina Baptist Hospital, Incorporated, was published in 1970. Carpenter's book recalls his thoughts about the medical school from the time he came to it in 1926 until 1963. His book covers the period during which the medical school went from a two-year program or "half school" as Wake Forest School of Medical Sciences (1902-1941) in the town of Wake Forest to a four-year program as Bowman Gray School of Medicine in Winston-Salem with its first class graduating in 1943.

—*The Miracle on Hawthorne Hill* by Dr. Manson Meads, retired dean of Bowman Gray School of Medicine of Wake Forest University, was published in 1988. Meads' book picks up the story of the Medical Center from the 1940s and goes through the 1980s. Meads succeeded Carpenter as dean in 1963 and as vice president of medical affairs in 1967. He was the first director of the Medical Center when these institutions were reorganized in 1974. He wrote *The Miracle on Hawthorne Hill* after he retired in 1983, hoping that a record of the past would "broaden the appreciation of what now is and point up inherent qualities that can usefully serve the future."

—*One Hundred Years of Medicine, Legacy, & Promise,* published in October 2002, celebrates Wake Forest University's journey into medicine. Through pictures and words, the book details through a timeline display the growth of a two-year college course into a four-year program known today as Wake Forest University School of Medicine. It illustrates the medical school's development, along with its teaching hospital, The North Carolina Baptist Hospitals, Incorporated, into one of the nation's major academic medical centers of excellence. Donna S. Garrison edited the centennial book. Dr. Frank James and Dr. Doug Maynard co-chaired the book's prepartion.

GLOSSARY

Here is a brief collection of technical terms prepared by Baptist Hospital and approved by the Office for Chief of Professional Services for patients and health care providers who encounter these phrases in the course of health care delivery.

—**Advance directive:** A document executed by the patient that expresses the patient's wishes regarding therapy when the patient becomes incompetent to make health care decisions. The document needs to be signed, witnessed, notarized. Living wills and health care powers of attorney are advance directives and both are recognized in North Carolina State law. A living will can apply to the patient's whose condition is terminable, incurable, or is in persistent vegetative state. The health care power of attorney establishes a proxy decisionmaker to make decisions the patient would have wanted.

—**Attending physician:** A member of the faculty of WFUSM who serves on the medical staff of The North Carolina Baptist Hospitals, Incorporated and is responsible for a patient's care.

—**A competent adult patient** is any adult patient of sound mind who is capable of making informed health care decisions and for whom a court has not appointed a guardian.

—**Concurring physician** is one who agrees with the assessment of the patient's condition as stated by the physician writing withhold or withdrawal therapy orders. The concurring physician must hold a North Carolina medical license and have permission to practice medicine at the Medical Center.

—**Decisional capacity** is the capacity and understanding to make and communicate health care decisions exercised by a person 18 or older.

—**Extraordinary means** (futile therapy) is any medical procedure or intervention that in the judgment of the physician would serve only to postpone artificially the moment of death by sustaining, restoring, or supplanting a vital function. It does not refer to the technological complexity of the intervention of any procedure. Therefore, for a patient who is terminally ill, extraordinary means may refer to antibiotics, blood transfusions, minor surgery, or artificial hydration or nutrition.

—**Health care power of attorney** means a written instrument, signed in the presence of two qualified witnesses and acknowledged before a notary public, pursuant to which an attorney-in-fact or agent is appointed to act for the patient in matters relating to the health care of the patient. Another term used for this instrument is durable power of attorney for health care.

—**Health care agent** means a person appointed as a health care attorney-in-fact. Another term used for this agent is health care proxy.

—**Persistent vegetative status** is a medical condition whereby, in the judgment of the attending physician, the patient suffers from or sustained complete loss of self-awareness cognition and without use of extraordinary means or artificial nutrition or hydration will succumb to death within a short period of time.

—**Resident physician** is a physician licensed in North Carolina to practice medicine while in training. Fellows are considered residents for the purpose of this policy.

—**Resuscitation** refers to the use of any therapeutic procedure or method to maintain life in the event of cardiac or respiratory failure. The most basic forms of resuscitation or an emergent condition include tracheal intubation with manually or mechanically assisted ventilation, cardiac massage, and electrical defibrillation or cardioversion. Depending on the situation, a wide range of other interventions also may be included in a resuscitation efforts: maintaining an adequate airway by suctioning of mouth, pharynx, and trachea; Heimlich maneuvers or ventilation by bag-valve mask; medical therapy including blood products, pressor substances, cardiac medication, dialysis, and surgery and diagnostic tests.

—**Terminal illness** is an incurable or irreversible condition that has a high probability of causing death within one year with or without treatment. Conditions such as persistent vegetative state or chronic dementia are not usually terminal. Determination of a terminal condition is the responsibility of the physician.

—**Withholding or withdrawing therapy** means a provision of medical therapy should always be decided on the basis of the benefit it gives to the patient and the standards of medical practice. Withholding therapy means not providing or discontinuing therapy. Withdrawing therapy means stopping or discontinuing therapy. There is no moral difference between withholding therapy determined to be extraordinary and withdrawing therapy determined to be extraordinary or futile.